my revision notes

WJEC GCSE
ADDITIONAL SCIENCE

Jeremy Pollard
Adrian Schmit

HODDER
EDUCATION
AN HACHETTE UK COMPANY

The publisher would like to thank the following for permission to reproduce copyright photographs:
p.18 *l* © Ingram Publishing Limited/Ultimate Lifestyle 06, *r* ©Photodisc/Getty Images/Business & Industry 1; **p.39** Juan Pablo Fuentes S – Fotolia; **p.42** © alessandrozocc – Fotolia.com; **p.43** FLPA/Bob Gibbons/ Holt; **p.44** FLPA/Nigel Cattlin; **p.45** Henrik Larsson – Fotolia; **p.50** Martyn F. Chillmaid; **p.51** Martyn F. Chillmaid; **p.58** Pascal Goetgheluck/Science Photo Library.

Although every effort has been made to ensure that website addresses are correct at time of going to press, Hodder Education cannot be held responsible for the content of any website mentioned. It is sometimes possible to find a relocated web page by typing in the address of the home page for a website in the URL window of your browser.

Orders: please contact Bookpoint Ltd, 130 Milton Park, Abingdon, Oxon OX14 4SB. Telephone: (44) 01235 827720. Fax: (44) 01235 400454. Lines are open 9.00–17.00, Monday to Saturday, with a 24-hour message answering service. Visit our website at www.hoddereducation.co.uk

Impression number	5	4	3	2	1
Year	2016	2015	2014	2013	2012

Cover photo © Gavin Kingcome/Science Photo Library
Illustrations by Barking Dog Art
Typeset in Cronospro-Lt 12 points by Datapage (India) Pvt. Ltd.
Printed in Spain
A catalogue record for this title is available from the British Library.
ISBN 978 1 444 171624

Get the most from this book

This book will help you revise the contents of the new WJEC GCSE Additional Science specification. You can use the contents list on pages 4 and 5 to plan your revision, topic by topic. Tick each box when you have:

1 revised and understood a topic
2 tested yourself
3 checked your answers online.

You can also keep track of your revision by ticking off each topic heading through the book. You may find it helpful to add your own notes as you work through each topic.

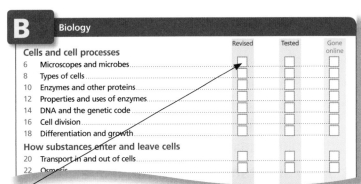

Tick to track your progress

Examiner tip

Throughout the book there are Examiner tips that explain how you can boost your final grade.

Higher tier

Some parts of the WJEC specification are tested only on higher-tier exam papers. These sections are highlighted using a red and yellow strip down the side of the page.

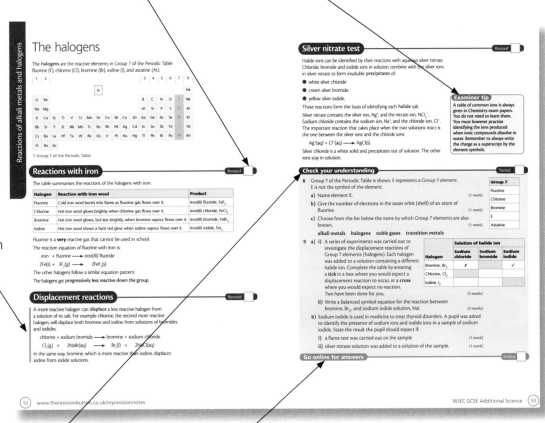

Check your understanding

Use these questions at the end of each section to make sure that you have understood every topic.

Go online

Go online to check your answers at
www.therevisionbutton.co.uk/myrevisionnotes

Contents and revision planner

B Biology

		Revised	Tested	Gone online
Cells and cell processes				
6	Microscopes and micro-organisms	☐	☐	☐
8	Types of cells	☐	☐	☐
10	Enzymes and other proteins	☐	☐	☐
12	Properties and uses of enzymes	☐	☐	☐
14	DNA and the genetic code	☐	☐	☐
16	Cell division	☐	☐	☐
18	Differentiation and growth	☐	☐	☐
How substances enter and leave cells				
20	Transport in and out of cells	☐	☐	☐
22	Osmosis	☐	☐	☐
Photosynthesis				
24	Photosynthesis	☐	☐	☐
26	Environmental factors and photosynthesis	☐	☐	☐
Respiration				
28	Respiration and life	☐	☐	☐
30	The human respiratory system	☐	☐	☐
32	Smoking and health	☐	☐	☐
Digestion				
34	Food and digestion	☐	☐	☐
36	The digestive system and enzymes	☐	☐	☐
Biodiversity and the environment				
38	Biodiversity	☐	☐	☐
40	Measuring biodiversity	☐	☐	☐
42	Biological control	☐	☐	☐
44	The capture–recapture technique	☐	☐	☐

C Chemistry

		Revised	Tested	Gone online
Atomic structure and the Periodic Table				
46	Atomic structure	☐	☐	☐
48	Atoms and the Periodic Table	☐	☐	☐
Reactions of alkali metals and halogens				
50	The alkali metals	☐	☐	☐
52	The halogens	☐	☐	☐
Chemical bonding and chemical change				
54	Chemical bonding 1	☐	☐	☐
56	Chemical bonding 2	☐	☐	☐
58	Smart materials	☐	☐	☐

P Physics

Microscopes and micro-organisms

Development of the microscope
Revised

There are many forms of life that are too small to see with the naked eye. They were only discovered after the invention of the microscope. As microscopes have become more advanced, the magnification that is possible has increased, and this has led to further discoveries about cells and microscopic life.

The standard microscopes used today in most laboratories pass light through material on a glass slide and use a system of lenses to view the image. The **light microscope** was invented around 1600, and over the next 400 years improvements in lens technology meant that the magnification increased (up to about ×1000) and the picture seen could be made clearer.

The **electron microscope**, invented in 1931, uses a beam of electrons instead of light, and this allows much greater magnifications – up to ×50 million.

A recent development is the use of lasers to build up an image via a computer by scanning an object in the microscope. This is known as **confocal laser scanning microscopy**. Its aim is not to increase magnification, but to produce clearer images.

Examiner tip

Most of this material was not included in the specification up to 2012. You will therefore not find questions on microscopes and the cell theory in past papers, although there may be questions about micro-organisms.

The cell theory
Revised

An early light microscope was used by Robert Hooke to discover cells in 1665, but it wasn't until the 1830s that scientists Matthias Schleiden and Theodor Schwann proposed the **cell theory** – that all living things are made of cells. Schleiden had been working on plants and Schwann on animal tissues, but they had found similar 'cellular' structures in both. Their idea of the cell as the basic unit of life was correct, although they did not know about cell division and thought that new cells formed in a way similar to the formation of crystals. The cell theory has been modified over the years by new discoveries. It now states:

1 All living organisms are composed of one or more cells.
2 The cell is the basic 'unit' of life.
3 Cells are formed from pre-existing cells during cell division.
4 Energy flow (the sequence of chemical reactions that create life) occurs within cells.
5 Heredity information (DNA) is passed on from cell to cell when cell division occurs.
6 All cells have the same basic chemical composition.

Micro-organisms

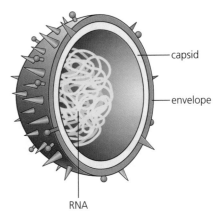

Micro-organisms are microscopic life forms. They include **bacteria**, **viruses**, **fungi** and **unicellular algae**.

Viruses are the smallest forms of life, and are so simple that it is not certain if they can really be called living things. They consist of some genetic material (DNA or RNA) inside a protein case. They can only reproduce inside another living cell, the 'host' cell. The release of the new viruses destroys the host cell, and the released viruses then attack new host cells.

Bacteria reproduce asexually by dividing into two. Bacteria are thought to have been the earliest forms of life.

Yeasts are microscopic fungi. They reproduce asexually by **budding** – growing a new cell from an existing one, after which the new cell breaks off.

The structure of the cells of bacteria, fungi and algae are dealt with in the next section.

↑**Cross-section through an influenza virus**

Check your understanding

1 There are three main types of micro-organism.

bacteria   fungi   viruses

a) Which micro-organism reproduces by dividing into two? *(1 mark)*

b) Which micro-organism can only reproduce inside a host cell? *(1 mark)*

c) Name the type of micro-organism shown in the diagram. (Not drawn to scale.) *(1 mark)*

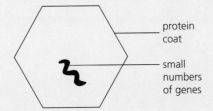

d) Which of the statements below is correct? *(1 mark)*

A Bacteria are smaller than viruses.

B Bacteria are larger than viruses.

C Bacteria are the same size as viruses.

2 The table below lists the features of three different types of micro-organism A, B and C.

Feature	Micro-organism A	Micro-organism B	Micro-organism C
Outer coat	Protein	Cell wall	Cell wall
Cytoplasm	No	Yes	Yes
Cell membrane	No	Yes	Yes
Nucleus	No	Yes	No distinct nucleus
Reproduction	Inside other cells	By budding	By dividing in two

From the information given in the table, name the group of micro-organisms to which A, B and C belong. *(3 marks)*

Go online for answers

Types of cells

Although all living things are made of cells, different cells show a lot of variation in structure. The cells of plants and animals show characteristic differences, and these differences can be used to distinguish the two types of cell under the microscope.

Plant and animal cells

The structures of a 'typical' animal cell and a 'typical' plant cell are shown in the diagram, although in both animals and plants different types of cell exist which vary in shape and size.

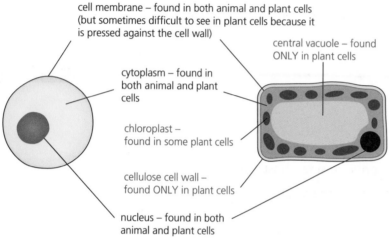

cell membrane – found in both animal and plant cells (but sometimes difficult to see in plant cells because it is pressed against the cell wall)

central vacuole – found ONLY in plant cells

cytoplasm – found in both animal and plant cells

chloroplast – found in some plant cells

cellulose cell wall – found ONLY in plant cells

nucleus – found in both animal and plant cells

↑ **Typical animal (left) and plant (right) cells**

> **Examiner tip**
>
> Cells are considered an 'easy' topic and are usually tested on the Foundation rather than the Higher paper. The questions nearly always ask you to identify features on a diagram, and to state differences between animal and plant cells.

The different features of these cells and their functions are shown in the table.

Feature	Animal or plant cell	Function
Nucleus	Both	Controls the activities of the cells (via DNA)
Cell membrane	Both	Controls which substances enter and leave the cell
Cytoplasm	Both	Where most of the chemical reactions in the cell take place
Cellulose cell wall	Plant cells	Supports the cell
Chloroplast	Some plant cells	Absorbs light for photosynthesis
Large central vacuole	Plant cells	Space filled with liquid sap which stores nutrients

Other types of cell

Microbes have different types of cells to plants and animals. The structures of bacterial cells, yeast (single-celled fungi) and algal cells are shown on the next page. A virus cannot really be called a cell.

Bacterial cell

● DNA is not contained in a nucleus.

● Capsule, flagella and pilus (not present in all bacteria).

● Cell wall is not made of cellulose.

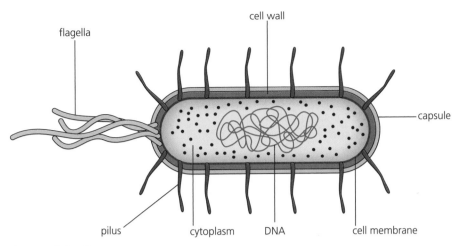

flagella

cell wall

capsule

pilus   cytoplasm   DNA   cell membrane

↑ **Bacterial cell**

Yeast cell

● Cell wall is not made of cellulose.

● Vacuole is smaller than the large central vacuole of a plant cell, and there may be more than one.

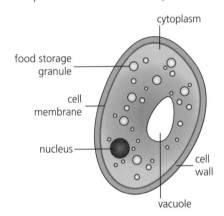

cytoplasm

food storage granule

cell membrane

nucleus

cell wall

vacuole

↑ **Yeast cell**

Algal cell

● Algal cells vary in basic structure.

● Most but not all have a flagellum.

● Some have a cellulose cell wall.

● The eyespot and vacuole are often absent.

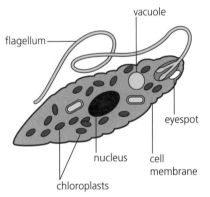

vacuole

flagellum

eyespot

nucleus   cell membrane

chloroplasts

↑ **Algal cell (Euglena)**

Examiner tip

You will never be asked in an exam question to draw any of these cells, only to identify and/or label them.

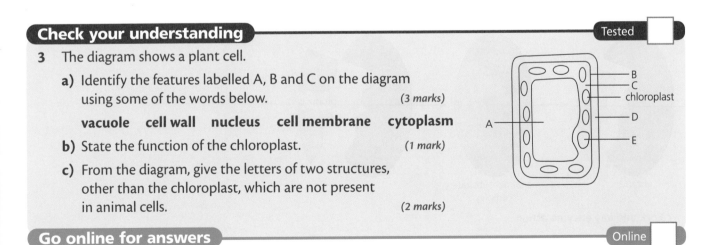

Check your understanding   Tested

3   The diagram shows a plant cell.

a) Identify the features labelled A, B and C on the diagram using some of the words below.   (3 marks)

    vacuole   **cell wall**   **nucleus**   **cell membrane**   **cytoplasm**

b) State the function of the chloroplast.   (1 mark)

c) From the diagram, give the letters of two structures, other than the chloroplast, which are not present in animal cells.   (2 marks)

Go online for answers   Online

Enzymes and other proteins

Proteins are important chemicals which are found in many forms in living things. One of the most important groups of proteins is **enzymes**. Enzymes control all the chemical reactions which occur in cells. Other important proteins include **hormones** and **muscle tissue**.

Structure of proteins — Revised

Proteins are made of a chain of smaller molecules called **amino acids**. A protein will have hundreds or even thousands of amino acids, and the sequence of the amino acids gives the protein its identity and properties.

The amino acid chain is folded in a particular way to form a 3D shape, which is different for every protein. The shape of enzyme molecules is particularly important, because the shape is essential to the function of the enzyme.

How enzymes work — Revised

A particular enzyme will only work on one chemical or a small group of similar chemicals. The substance that an enzyme works on is called its **substrate**. The enzyme has to make contact with its substrate and attach to it. For that to happen, the enzyme and substrate shapes have to match, so that they can lock together.

The place on the enzyme where the substrate attaches is called the **active site**. Enzymes are **specific** (i.e. they only work on one type of substrate) because the substrate shape has to match the shape of the active site.

When the enzyme and substrate are locked together, the combined structure is called an **enzyme–substrate complex**.

This explanation of how enzymes work by attaching to a matching substrate is called the **lock and key theory**, because they fit together like a lock and key. Just as a key will open only one lock, so an enzyme will only work on one type of substrate. Note that the enzyme and its substrate only join together; they do not react with each other.

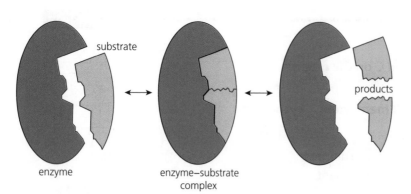

substrate

products

enzyme

enzyme–substrate complex

↑ **Lock and key enzyme action**

Properties of enzymes

Revised

- Enzymes are **biological catalysts** – they speed up chemical reactions without taking part in the reaction.

- Each enzyme has its own **optimum** pH and temperature (optimum means the best value for the enzyme to work).

- Enzymes are **denatured** (destroyed) by high temperatures, because the heat breaks the chemical bonds that hold the enzyme's active site in shape. All enzymes are denatured by boiling.

- If the pH is very far from the optimum, the enzyme may be denatured.

> **Examiner tip**
> Never say that an enzyme is 'killed' by boiling. This will always result in 0 marks. An enzyme is not alive (it is a chemical) and so cannot be killed.

Check your understanding

Tested

4 The enzyme catalase can only work on one substrate (hydrogen peroxide). Explain the reason for this. *(6 marks QWC)*

5 The diagram shows an enzyme working.

   a) Identify the labels A, B and C on the diagram. *(3 marks)*

   b) Explain why the enzyme will no longer work if it is boiled. *(2 marks)*

   c) An enzyme is described as a 'catalyst'. What does this mean? *(1 mark)*

   d) Complete the passage below about enzymes:

   All enzymes belong to the same chemical group (_____). They are made from a long chain of _____. This chain is folded in a particular way to give the enzyme a shape which allows it to fit together with its _____. *(3 marks)*

6 An experiment was done to study the effect of amylase enzyme on starch. A plate of starch agar had a 'well' cut into it and this was filled with amylase enzyme. After half an hour, iodine was added to the agar plate. Iodine stains the starch blue-black. The results are shown in the diagram.

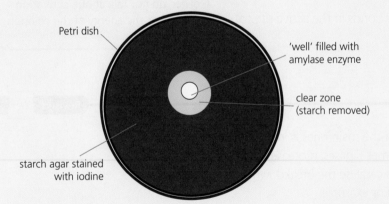

   a) State whether each of the following statements is **true** or **false**.

   i) Starch is the substrate for amylase. *(1 mark)*

   ii) Starch reacts with amylase. *(1 mark)*

   iii) The amylase has removed all the starch. *(1 mark)*

   iv) Amylase catalyses the breakdown of starch. *(1 mark)*

   b) Suggest a way in which scientists might measure the rate of the enzyme controlled reaction in this experiment. *(2 marks)*

Go online for answers

Online

Properties and uses of enzymes

Enzymes and temperature

The rate of an enzyme-controlled reaction will speed up with increasing temperature, up until the point where the heat denatures the enzyme.

The graph below shows the effect of temperature on an enzyme. The optimum temperature and the temperature which causes denaturation will vary from enzyme to enzyme.

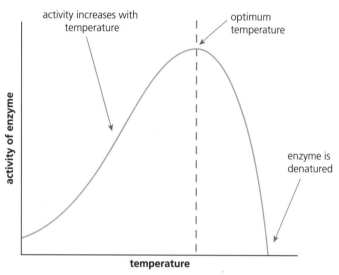

↑ **The effect of temperature on enzyme activity**

The increase in activity with temperature is because the heat is making the enzyme and substrate molecules move faster and therefore they will collide more often, allowing them to lock together.

The enzyme denatures when the heat causes bonds in the active site to break, changing its shape.

Examiner tip

As the enzyme and the substrate do not react chemically with each other, do not talk about 'activation energy' or the energy of the collision in this context.

Uses of enzymes

Enzymes have many commercial uses. One of the main ones is in biological washing detergents. Digestive enzymes (lipases, proteases and carbohydrases) are put into the detergents to catalyse the breakdown of stains that are otherwise difficult to remove. For example:

● Greases (lipids) are broken down by lipases.

● Grass stains (proteins) are broken down by proteases.

If enzymes were not used, the wash would have to be carried out at a higher temperature, which would require more energy.

7　**a)**　Complete the following sentences using some of the words in the list:

protein　**increase**　**decrease**　**chemical**　**temperature**

Enzymes are a type of _____. They _____ the rate of _____ reactions in living cells. Each works best at a particular _____ and pH value.　　　　　　　　*(4 marks)*

b)　What happens to enzymes at 100 °C?　　　　　　　　*(1 mark)*

c)　The graph shows the activity of an enzyme at different pH values.

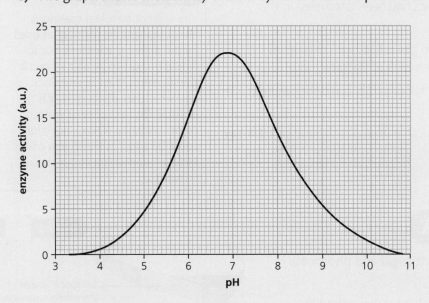

From the graph:

i)　At which pH value does this enzyme work best?　　　*(1 mark)*

ii)　Give the activity of the enzyme at pH 5.5.　　　　　*(1 mark)*

8　Biological washing powder was used to wash several pieces of cloth, which had identical stains on them, at different temperatures. The results are shown below.

A: 10 °C　　B: 30 °C　　C: 40 °C　　D: 60 °C　　Unwashed control

a)　What ingredient is present in the biological washing powder to break down stains, which is **not** present in non-biological washing powder?　*(1 mark)*

b)　At what temperature would you suggest clothes should be washed using this washing powder?　　　　　　　　*(2 marks)*

c)　Explain the results at 10 °C and at 60 °C.　　　　　　*(2 marks)*

d)　Suggest **two** variables the scientists doing this experiment should control in order to ensure a fair test.　　　　　　　　*(2 marks)*

e)　Why was it necessary to have an unwashed control?　　*(1 mark)*

Go online for answers　　　　　　　　　　　　Online

DNA and the genetic code

The discovery of DNA

Scientists **Francis Crick** and **James Watson** are credited with the discovery of the structure of DNA in 1953. However, they did not make this discovery on their own. Other scientists were involved, either directly or by having done preparatory work.

- DNA is a **nucleic acid**. Nucleic acids had been discovered in the mid-19th century.
- The link between nucleic acids and genes had been discovered by Oswald Avery in 1944, using experiments on bacteria.
- Watson and Crick used chemical theory and ball-and-stick atomic models to work out the structure.
- The data to allow them to do this came from a technique called **X-ray crystallography** used by two other scientists, Maurice Wilkins and Rosalind Franklin.

Examiner tip

You will not be asked questions about the specific techniques used by the different scientists, but it would be best to be able to recall the names of Watson and Crick and what they discovered. It is possible that a quality of written communication (QWC) question could be asked in which you could include information about these scientists.

The structure of DNA

DNA has two long chains of alternating **sugar** and **phosphate** molecules.

- The two chains are twisted into a shape called a **double helix**, which is an interlocking spiral (see diagram).
- These chains are joined by **bases**.
- There are four bases: **adenine (A)**, **cytosine (C)**, **guanine (G)** and **thymine (T)**.
- The order in which these bases occur along the chain forms a 'code', which determines the order in which different amino acids are linked together to form different proteins.
- Adenine A always joins in a pair to thymine T, and cytosine C always joins in a pair to guanine G (see diagram).
- It is a sequence of three bases along the DNA chain which 'codes' for each amino acid. This is called a **triplet code**.

The structure of DNA is shown in the diagram.

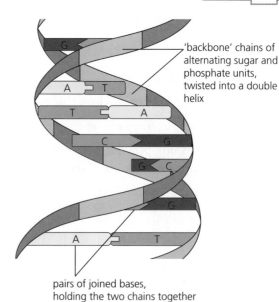

'backbone' chains of alternating sugar and phosphate units, twisted into a double helix

pairs of joined bases, holding the two chains together

↑ **DNA structure**

The importance of DNA

DNA is the shortened name of a chemical called deoxyribose nucleic acid, although it is always known just as DNA. It is one of the most important chemicals known to man. It is the chemical which provides 'instructions' for every cell to work. It does this by determining which **amino acids** are linked together to form the different proteins that the cell needs in order to work. Enzymes are proteins which control all the chemical reactions of life. Since the DNA controls which proteins (and so which enzymes) a cell makes, it indirectly controls all the activities in the cell.

Examiner tip

The information on this topic you are required to know is different from what was in the previous specification, so past papers for Additional Science before 2013 contain no questions on this material.

Check your understanding

9 The DNA molecule consists of two strands, twisted into a double helix shape.

   a) Which **two** types of molecule are found in the strands? *(2 marks)*

   b) Which type of chemical holds the two chains together? *(1 mark)*

   c) DNA 'codes' for the formation of proteins. How does it do this? *(3 marks)*

   d) Which **two** scientists discovered the structure of the DNA molecule? *(2 marks)*

10 The diagram below shows a section of DNA.

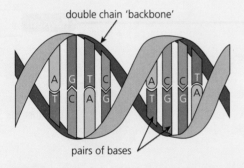

double chain 'backbone'

pairs of bases

   a) What name is given to the shape formed by the DNA's chains? *(1 mark)*

   b) What **two** types of molecule make up these chains? *(2 marks)*

   c) The sequence of different bases along the DNA molecule forms a 'code'. What does this code determine? *(2 marks)*

   d) What are the names of the four bases found in DNA? *(4 marks)*

11 The discovery of the structure of DNA required the collaboration of different scientists using a variety of techniques. Describe how this came about. *(6 marks QWC)*

Go online for answers

Online

Cell division

Types of cell division

Throughout the life of an organism, new cells are constantly being formed from old cells by the process of **cell division**. These new cells may be required for growth, for repair of tissues, for the replacement of old cells or for the formation of sex cells. In both animals and plants, there are two types of cell division: **mitosis** and **meiosis**. Mitosis is the 'normal' type of cell division, and meiosis is a special type of cell division that only happens when sex cells (gametes) are made.

In cell division, the original cell is always called the **mother** cell, and the new cells formed are called the **daughter** cells.

> **Examiner tip**
>
> The words mitosis and meiosis are very similar. Make sure you spell them correctly in exam answers – for example, if you write 'miosis' the examiner cannot be certain if you mean mitosis or meiosis, and will not give a mark.

Mitosis

The most common form of cell division is called mitosis. This produces new cells for growth, for repair of tissues and to replace worn out cells. The **chromosomes** of a cell carry the genes, so it is essential that each new cell is provided with a set of chromosomes. To do this, the chromosomes of the 'mother' cell duplicate and each new cell receives one of the duplicate sets. The features of mitosis are as follows.

- Mitosis takes place in all tissues of the plant and animal body, except those that form sex cells (gametes).
- It provides cells for growth, repair, and for the replacement of old cells.
- Two new daughter cells are formed.
- Each of the new cells has a full set of chromosomes.
- The new cells are **genetically identical** to each other and to the mother cell.
- The new cells are of the same type as the mother cell.

> **Examiner tip**
>
> Each type of cell division occurs in several stages. You do not have to know those stages for the exam.

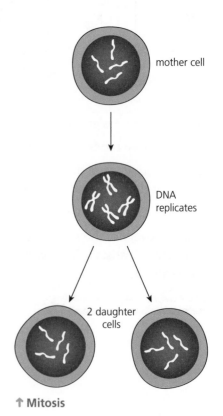

mother cell

DNA replicates

2 daughter cells

↑ **Mitosis**

When **gametes** (e.g. sperm cells, egg cells, pollen) are formed a different type of division, meiosis, takes place. If the gametes each received a full set of chromosomes, when fertilisation occurred the new organism would have twice the normal number of chromosomes, and would not survive. Meiosis therefore differs from mitosis in a number of ways.

● Meiosis only takes place in tissues which form sex cells/gametes.

● Four cells are formed, because meiosis is a double division, i.e. one division is immediately followed by a second one.

● Each of the daughter cells has a half set of chromosomes. The chromosome numbers are halved in the first of the two divisions.

● Each of the new cells is **genetically different**.

● The new cells change (**differentiate**) into gametes, which are different from the mother cell.

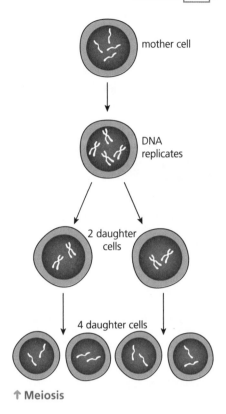

mother cell

DNA replicates

2 daughter cells

4 daughter cells

↑ **Meiosis**

12 Ferret body cells contain 40 chromosomes.

a) Identify the correct number of chromosomes in each box (A–D) below. *(2 marks)*

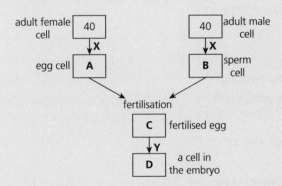

b) Name the type of cell division that is taking place at

    i) stage X *(1 mark)*

    ii) stage Y. *(1 mark)*

13 There are two different types of cell division: mitosis and meiosis. Listed below are a number of features of cell division. For each one, state whether it is a feature of **mitosis** or **meiosis**.

a) Four new cells are formed from one original cell. *(1 mark)*

b) The new cells are genetically different. *(1 mark)*

c) Takes place in normal body cells. *(1 mark)*

d) The new cells formed have a half set of chromosomes. *(1 mark)*

e) The new cells are of the same type as the mother cell. *(1 mark)*

Go online for answers
Online

Differentiation and growth

Most living things start life as a fertilised egg, or **zygote**. This single cell gives rise to the billions of cells that make up larger living things. The multiplication of cells results in **growth** – the organism gets bigger. In addition, the cells develop into different types of cells, each specialised for its particular purpose. The specialisation is called **differentiation**.

Patterns of growth

Animals and plants have different patterns of growth and development, which are summarised in the table.

Animals	Plants
All regions of the body grow.	Growth is restricted to special growing points, called **meristems**. The main ones are at the tips of the roots and the shoots.
Tend to grow to a certain size and then stop growing.	Usually grow throughout their life.
Usually have a compact growth form (i.e. non-branching).	Usually have a spreading, branched growth form.

For animals and plants, the pattern of growth is well suited to their life, as follows.

Animals

● Animals have a greater variety of organs and tissues than plants. Growing all over ensures that all of these organs grow in conjunction with each other.

● Growing for a time and then stopping allows animals to use energy for other purposes (e.g. movement).

Plants

● The main requirements for a plant are light and water. The growing points at the tip of the shoot and root allow the plant to grow up towards the light, and down towards soil water.

● The spreading body form of plants allows a greater surface area for absorbing light. Animals don't need this.

● Parts of plants are often eaten by animals. Growing throughout their life allows plants to replace the eaten parts.

↑ **Humans and plants grow in very different ways**

Differentiation and stem cells

Revised

Cells differentiate after being formed by cell division. Once they have become specialised, most cannot differentiate any further. A few cells retain the ability to differentiate, however. These are called **stem cells**. Stem cells are found in both animals and plants:

- in embryos
- in certain adult tissues (e.g. bone marrow)
- in the growing points (meristems) of plants.

Using human stem cells

Revised

Human stem cells are thought to have great potential for curing many human conditions, as they can be used to replace damaged cells of many different types. Embryonic stem cells are slightly more useful than adult stem cells, because they have greater powers of differentiation. The use of embryonic stem cells is opposed by some people because the embryo is destroyed in the process. The embryos used are grown in the laboratory and are not the result of natural conception, so others feel that their use is justified.

Examiner tip

In questions about stem cells you may have to consider the ethical issues of their use. This is not a case of knowing facts but of being familiar with the issues. Internet research is useful here.

Check your understanding

Tested

14 'Adult' stem cells are present in a child's baby teeth. It is now possible to store stem cells. When a baby tooth falls out, it is sealed in a container of milk and sent to a laboratory where the stem cells are allowed to multiply until they reach approximately one million cells. These cells are then stored in liquid nitrogen at −190 °C.

    a) What is a stem cell? *(1 mark)*

    b) State **one** advantage to a person of storing their own stem cells. *(1 mark)*

    c) In a plant, what name is given to the areas of growth where stem cells are formed? *(1 mark)*

15 Stem cells could be very helpful in repairing damaged cells and curing conditions that result from cell damage, yet some people object to their use. Suggest reasons for this. *(6 marks QWC)*

Go online for answers

Online

Transport in and out of cells

Transport processes

Many chemicals travel into and out of cells through the cell membrane. They move by one of three processes:

- **Diffusion**: Substances move from an area of higher concentration to an area of lower concentration.

- **Osmosis**: This is a special term for the diffusion of water molecules through the cell membrane.

- **Active transport**: This is the 'pumping' of substances from an area of lower concentration to an area of higher concentration (i.e. the opposite way to diffusion) using energy from the cell.

Diffusion

Molecules move **randomly** – they don't 'know' where they are going. However, because there is more 'room' to move in areas of lower concentration, their natural tendency is to spread out from areas of higher concentration to areas of lower concentration.

Diffusion does not require energy, but only certain substances can pass through the membrane in this way. The membrane is **selectively permeable**, which means it lets certain substances through but stops others. Water, oxygen and carbon dioxide are three important substances that can diffuse in and out of cells. Remember that diffusion of water into and out of cells is always called osmosis. This is dealt with in the next section.

> **Examiner tip**
>
> When answering questions about diffusion and osmosis remember the idea of **net** movement. The molecules move in all directions but, on balance, the overall (net) movement is from high to low concentration.

Active transport

Sometimes a cell needs to move a substance up a **concentration gradient**, that is, from an area of low concentration to an area of high concentration. This will not happen naturally, because diffusion works in the opposite direction. In order to move chemicals in this way, the cell has to use energy to 'pump' the substance up the gradient. This process is called active transport. It is usually used to move substances into the cell rather than out of it.

Concentration gradients

Movement into and out of cells is often described in terms of 'concentration gradients'. These occur where substances are present in varying concentrations. A gradient is a slope between a high value and a low value. Movement can occur down a concentration gradient by diffusion/osmosis or up it by active transport.

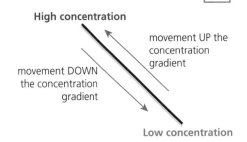

↑ **Movement along a concentration gradient**

Check your understanding

16 The diagram shows an animal cell, and the levels of various substances inside and outside it.

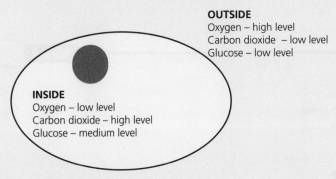

OUTSIDE
Oxygen – high level
Carbon dioxide – low level
Glucose – low level

INSIDE
Oxygen – low level
Carbon dioxide – high level
Glucose – medium level

a) In which direction (into or out of the cell) will the net movement of these molecules occur?

   i) Oxygen   *(1 mark)*

   ii) Carbon dioxide   *(1 mark)*

b) What is the name of the process that results in the movement of oxygen and carbon dioxide?   *(1 mark)*

c) The cell needs to take in glucose. Why will this process require energy?   *(1 mark)*

d) What is the name of the process that would cause glucose to be absorbed into this cell?   *(1 mark)*

17 Respiration occurs in all cells. It uses oxygen and produces carbon dioxide. The oxygen and carbon dioxide levels in two cells, A and B, and a blood capillary that runs alongside both cells, are given in the table.

Substance	Cell A	Cell B	Blood capillary
Oxygen	3%	4%	4%
Carbon dioxide	6%	5%	4%

State whether each of the statements below is **true** or **false**.

a) Oxygen will move from cell A into the blood.   *(1 mark)*

b) Oxygen will move from the blood into cell B.   *(1 mark)*

c) Carbon dioxide will move from cell B into the blood.   *(1 mark)*

d) Cell A will absorb oxygen from the blood and will pass carbon dioxide into the blood.   *(1 mark)*

e) There will be no net movement of oxygen into or out of the blood from cell B.   *(1 mark)*

Go online for answers

Online

Osmosis

Definition of osmosis

Osmosis is the diffusion of water through a selectively permeable membrane. The net movement is from a more dilute solution (which has more water) to a more concentrated solution (which has less water).

For the term osmosis to be used, the substance moving has to be water and it has to move through a membrane. The membrane is described as either **selectively permeable** or **partially permeable**. Both terms mean that it lets certain things through and keeps others out. In experiments, **visking tubing**, which acts like a selectively permeable membrane, is often used to model osmosis.

> **Examiner tip**
>
> It is acceptable to talk of a dilute solution having a 'higher concentration of water' and a concentrated solution having a 'lower concentration of water', although usually the term concentration refers to the solute.

How osmosis works

The mechanism of osmosis is shown in the diagram.

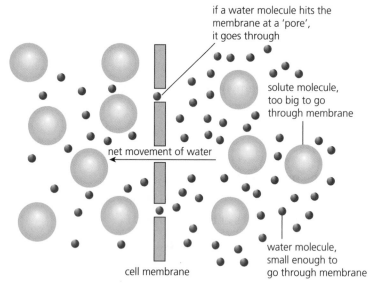

if a water molecule hits the membrane at a 'pore', it goes through

solute molecule, too big to go through membrane

net movement of water

water molecule, small enough to go through membrane

cell membrane

CONCENTRATED SOLUTION
fewer water molecules

DILUTE SOLUTION
more water molecules

↑ **The process of osmosis**

The molecules are moving all the time, and will come in contact with the membrane. If a molecule hits a 'pore', it will go through if it is a water molecule, but not if it is a solute molecule. As there are more water molecules in the dilute solution, more molecules will go through from that side than in the reverse direction. Although water moves in both directions, the **net movement** of water is from the more dilute solution to the more concentrated solution.

> **Examiner tip**
>
> Remember that osmosis is a two-way process. If the concentration inside and outside of the cell is the same, osmosis does not stop, but the movement in and out of the cell is balanced and there is no **net** movement of water.

If a cell is placed in water, the net movement of water will be into the cell. No matter how much water moves in, though, the solution inside the cell will always be more concentrated than water. Water will continue to move in, and eventually an animal cell will burst. Plant cells do not burst because their cell wall is strong enough to prevent it.

When put in a concentrated solution, the cytoplasm of both animal and plant cells will shrivel due to loss of water and the cell may die. In plant cells, the cytoplasm may pull away from the cell wall, a condition known as **plasmolysis**.

Check your understanding ——————————————— Tested

18 Students investigated the effect of sugar solution on potato tissue in the following way. Cylinders of potato of constant size were cut and covered by a range of sugar solutions of different concentrations (see diagram).

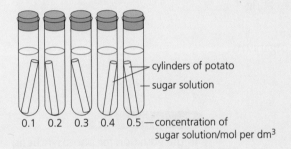

0.1 0.2 0.3 0.4 0.5 —concentration of sugar solution/mol per dm³

cylinders of potato
sugar solution

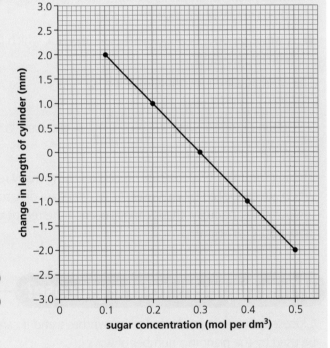

The lengths of the potato cylinders were measured at the start and after 30 minutes in the solutions. The graph shows the changes in length after 30 minutes in the solution.

a) **i)** What concentration of sugar solution is the same as the concentration of the cell sap of the potatoes? *(1 mark)*

    ii) Explain your answer to part **(i)**. *(1 mark)*

b) What would be the expected change in length of a potato cylinder in sugar solution at a concentration of 0.25 mol per dm³? *(1 mark)*

c) Explain the change in length of the potato cylinders when they were placed in sugar solution of concentration 0.5 mol per dm³. *(6 marks QWC)*

Go online for answers ——————————————— Online

Photosynthesis

The process of photosynthesis

Photosynthesis is the process by which green plants make food, using raw materials from the atmosphere and energy from sunlight. Without photosynthesis, no life could exist on the planet.

- All life needs energy, and the only supply of useable energy that the planet gets is sunlight. Green plants (and a few bacteria) are the only organisms that can use this energy directly.

- They can do this because they have **chlorophyll** which can absorb light.

- Photosynthesis takes place in the green parts of the plant, and mostly in the leaves. The green parts contain cells with chlorophyll in their **chloroplasts**.

- Plants make food (**glucose**) by photosynthesis for their own use, but animals depend on plants for food, either by eating them or eating other animals which have eaten plants.

- A waste product of photosynthesis is **oxygen**, which living organisms need for respiration.

The word equation for photosynthesis is:

$$\text{carbon dioxide} + \text{water} \xrightarrow[\text{chlorophyll}]{\text{sunlight}} \text{glucose} + \text{oxygen}$$

This is a summary of a complex process involving many reactions, all of which are controlled by **enzymes**. As enzymes are denatured by high temperatures, photosynthesis cannot occur if the temperature is very high (about 50 °C or above).

> **Examiner tip**
>
> In the equation for photosynthesis, the inclusion of chlorophyll and sunlight are important. They are not reactants in the process, though, and so should be written on the arrow.

What happens to the glucose?

Glucose is the main product of photosynthesis, and it can be used by the plant in a number of ways:

- It can be used directly to provide energy by **respiration**.

- It can be used to make other substances such as **proteins** (for new cells) or **cellulose** (for cell walls). Proteins also require a supply of nitrogen and this comes from nitrates in the soil.

- It may be **transported** from the leaves to other parts of the plant (to growing points).

- Any excess glucose is stored in the leaf cells as **starch**.

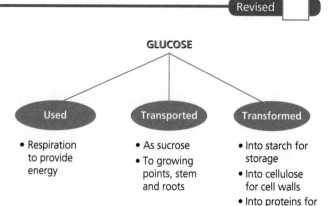

↑ The fate of the glucose made in photosynthesis

Testing for photosynthesis

When testing a leaf to see if photosynthesis has occurred, scientists test for starch, not for glucose. This is because the glucose is rapidly used, changed into starch or transported. It is easier to test for the starch that has been stored rather than the sugar. However, the starch store has to be used up by keeping the plant in the dark for a day or two (**de-starching**) in order to be certain that what is found is new starch, formed by photosynthesis during the experiment.

Examiner tip

Photosynthesis questions often link with a knowledge of respiration as well, as in Question **19** here.

Check your understanding

19 a) Fill in the blanks in the passage below by using some of the words given. *(4 marks)*

Sun oxygen chloroplasts nucleus water carbon dioxide

Green plants make their own food from _____ that is absorbed by the roots, _____ from the air, and light energy from the _____, which is absorbed by the _____ in a leaf cell.

b) Three test tubes were set up as shown in the diagram.

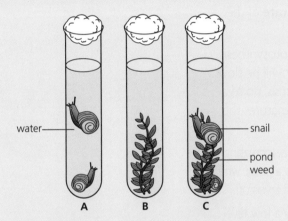

water —

snail

pond weed

A   B   C

They were then left in the light for 6 hours.

The tubes were then tested for carbon dioxide concentration.

i) Which tube had the highest concentration of carbon dioxide? Explain your answer. *(2 marks)*

ii) Which tube had the lowest concentration of carbon dioxide? Explain your answer. *(2 marks)*

Go online for answers

Online

Environmental factors and photosynthesis

Factors needed for photosynthesis

The following factors are needed for photosynthesis:

- **Light**, which provides the energy needed to make carbohydrates.
- **Carbon dioxide** from the air, as it is a raw material for the manufacture of carbohydrates.
- **Water** from the soil, the other raw material for photosynthesis.
- **Chlorophyll**, in the chloroplasts of the leaf cells, to absorb the light energy.
- A **suitable temperature**, so that the enzymes which control photosynthesis can work well.

> **Examiner tip**
>
> Pay close attention to the wording of questions. If they ask for **environmental** factors needed for photosynthesis, do not include chlorophyll – it is an internal factor, not provided from the environment.

Factors affecting the rate of photosynthesis

Not all of the factors needed for photosynthesis affect the **rate** of the process. Those that do are the following:

- **Temperature**. This affects the enzymes that control photosynthesis. At low temperatures, photosynthesis will not happen or will be slow. As temperature increases, so will the rate of photosynthesis, up to a point when the temperature becomes so high that it denatures the enzymes, stopping photosynthesis.
- **Light intensity**. This provides the energy for photosynthesis. Increasing the light intensity will increase the rate of photosynthesis, up to a point where there is as much light as can be absorbed and the rate then levels off.
- **Level of carbon dioxide**. The atmosphere contains only a low level of carbon dioxide (around 0.04%) and so increasing the level will allow a higher rate of photosynthesis. Eventually the rate will level off when there is enough carbon dioxide for the plant's needs.

Water does not affect the rate of photosynthesis because, if there is enough water for the plant to survive, there is plenty for photosynthesis. Adding extra makes no difference. Chlorophyll does not affect the rate because the amount in a plant at any one time cannot be changed.

Limiting factors

A **limiting factor** is the factor that is controlling the rate of photosynthesis at a given time, and the one that will, if increased, boost the rate. At night, light will be the limiting factor. During the day, it is usually carbon dioxide, though it may be temperature during the winter.

Photosynthesis experiments

You need to know the following techniques:

- **Testing leaves for starch** to see if photosynthesis has occurred. It involves boiling the leaf in alcohol to remove the colour, then staining with iodine; blue-black indicates starch (which is how glucose is stored).

- **Removing carbon dioxide** with sodium hydroxide solution, to test the need for carbon dioxide in photosynthesis.

- **Using oxygen and carbon dioxide sensors** to monitor the rate of photosynthesis.

Check your understanding

20 A farmer wanted to increase the yield of strawberries grown in his greenhouse.

An advisor calculated the mean level of carbon dioxide in the air in the greenhouse over a 24-hour period. He compared the mean carbon dioxide level in the greenhouse with the carbon dioxide graph below, and marked it on the graph.

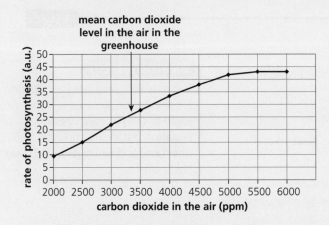

a) Why did the advisor measure the mean concentration of carbon dioxide in the air over a 24-hour period, rather than taking a single reading at a particular time during the 24-hour period? *(1 mark)*

b) i) Using the graph, draw a conclusion about the rate of photosynthesis of the strawberry plants in the farmer's greenhouse. *(1 mark)*

ii) Using only the graph, what advice would you give the farmer in order to gain a maximum yield of strawberries? *(2 marks)*

Go online for answers

Online

Respiration and life

What do we mean by respiration?

Respiration is a feature of **all** living things. It is the process that occurs inside cells to release the **energy** from food substances. This energy is needed for all life processes.

Normally, **oxygen** is used in the series of chemical reactions that make up respiration. This is **aerobic respiration**.

When there is not enough oxygen available, cells may switch to another form of respiration, **anaerobic respiration**, which does not require oxygen but releases less energy. All of the chemical reactions in respiration are controlled by **enzymes**.

Respiration is not breathing. Breathing is simply the process that gets oxygen into the body for respiration, and it only occurs in some animals.

Aerobic respiration

The word equation for aerobic respiration is:

glucose + oxygen $\longrightarrow$ carbon dioxide + water + ENERGY

- Respiration is not just a single reaction, but a complex series of reactions. The equation just summarises the process.
- Not all of the energy is useful. Some is always lost as **heat** to the surroundings.
- The rate of respiration can be found by measuring the amount of carbon dioxide or heat given off in a certain time, or by measuring the oxygen used in a given time.

> **Examiner tip**
> It is easy to remember the equation for respiration, because it is the same as the photosynthesis equation but in the opposite direction (and without the light and chlorophyll).

Anaerobic respiration

In the absence of oxygen, anaerobic respiration may occur. This is less **efficient** than aerobic respiration: less energy is released per molecule of glucose.

The process is different in animals and in yeast (which is a microscopic fungus).

Anaerobic respiration in animals

glucose $\longrightarrow$ lactic acid + ENERGY

- This can occur in human muscle cells during vigorous exercise, when the demand for oxygen is greater than the lungs can supply.
- The shortage of oxygen in such situations is called an **oxygen debt**.
- The body 'pays back' the oxygen debt by breathing faster and deeper for a while after the exercise has finished.
- The extra oxygen taken in in this way breaks down the lactic acid into carbon dioxide and water.

Anaerobic respiration in yeast

glucose ⟶ ethanol + carbon dioxide + ENERGY

- Ethanol is an **alcohol**; this process is used to brew alcoholic drinks.

- Note that carbon dioxide is produced by anaerobic respiration in yeast, but not in animals.

- Anaerobic respiration in yeast is known as **fermentation**.

Check your understanding   Tested

21 This is a diagram of a muscle cell.

Substances X and Y move into muscle cells from the blood.
In the cells, they react to release energy.

a) Name the chemical reaction which releases energy.   *(1 mark)*

b) Name a type of energy that is lost from the muscle cell during this reaction.   *(1 mark)*

c) Name substances X and Y.   *(2 marks)*

22 A sprinter starts a race. The simplified diagram represents respiration in his muscle cells.

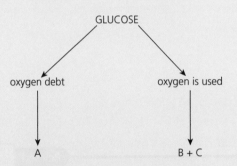

a) Name substances A, B and C.   *(3 marks)*

b) Why is aerobic respiration more efficient than anaerobic respiration?   *(1 mark)*

c) Which of the following is the most suitable description of 'oxygen debt'?   *(1 mark)*

    A The body's oxygen supply exceeds its demand.

    B More oxygen is breathed out than is breathed in.

    C The body's oxygen demand exceeds its supply.

    D There is less oxygen in the air than carbon dioxide.

Go online for answers   Online

The human respiratory system

The need for a respiratory system

The job of the respiratory system is to get **oxygen** into the blood, to be carried around the body for use in respiration, and to remove waste **carbon dioxide** from the blood. Large animals such as humans need a respiratory system because diffusion of oxygen through the body surface (as in very small animals) would be too slow to supply the innermost tissues. The organs of gas exchange in humans are the lungs.

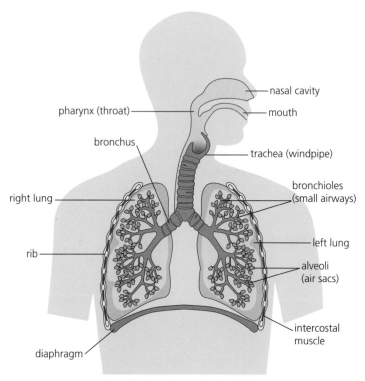

nasal cavity

pharynx (throat)

mouth

bronchus

trachea (windpipe)

bronchioles (small airways)

right lung

left lung

rib

alveoli (air sacs)

intercostal muscle

diaphragm

⬆ **The human respiratory system**

The alveoli

The **alveoli** (singular: alveolus) are air sacs, at the end of the **bronchioles**, where gas exchange takes place.

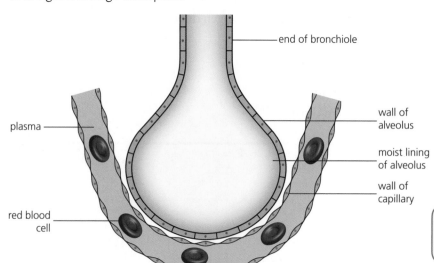

end of bronchiole

plasma

wall of alveolus

moist lining of alveolus

wall of capillary

red blood cell

⬆ **An alveolus**

> **Examiner tip**
>
> In exams, you will be expected to use the term alveolus, not 'air sac'.

Alveoli are adapted for gas exchange in the following ways:

● The large number of alveoli provides a **large surface area** for gas exchange.

● The **thin walls** of the alveoli mean that gases can pass through easily and quickly.

● The **moist lining** allows oxygen to dissolve, which is necessary before it can diffuse through the wall.

● The alveoli have a **good blood supply**, so that more gases can be exchanged.

Differences between inspired and expired air   Revised

Inspired air is air breathed in; **expired** air is air breathed out. The body absorbs oxygen from inspired air, and adds carbon dioxide and water vapour before breathing it out. So expired air differs from inspired air. Expired air:

● has less oxygen

● has more carbon dioxide

● has more water vapour.

The breathing mechanism   Revised

Breathing is caused by movements of the rib cage and the diaphragm. The sequence is as follows:

1 The diaphragm moves down and the rib cage moves up and out.

2 This causes an increase in the volume of the thorax (thoracic cavity).

3 The increased volume of the thorax means its pressure is lower.

4 The lower pressure allows the lungs to expand. Air is drawn in.

5 The diaphragm moves upwards and the ribcage moves in and down.

6 This decreases the volume and increases the pressure in the thorax.

7 The increased pressure compresses the lungs and air is pushed out.

Check your understanding   Tested

23 The apparatus shown is used as a model of the breathing mechanism in humans. When the plastic sheet is pulled downwards, the balloons expand. When it is pushed upwards, the balloons collapse.

   a) In the model, which part represents:

    i) the lungs   *(1 mark)*

    ii) the trachea   *(1 mark)*

    iii) the diaphragm?   *(1 mark)*

   b) Explain why the balloons expand when the sheet is pulled downwards.   *(3 marks)*

   c) State **one** way in which this model of the human respiratory system is inaccurate.   *(1 mark)*

glass tubing
balloon
bell jar
plastic sheet

Go online for answers   Online

Smoking and health

Smoking and the lungs

The lining of the respiratory system produces sticky **mucus**. This traps dust and bacteria from the air breathed in. The cells lining the trachea and bronchioles have delicate hair-like structures called **cilia**, which move, constantly shifting the mucus to the top of the trachea, where it is swallowed.

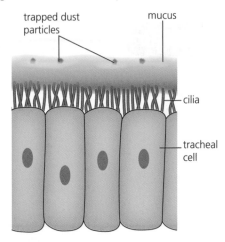

trapped dust particles

mucus

cilia

tracheal cell

↑ **Tracheal cells with cilia**

Inhalation of smoke causes paralysis of the cilia. The mucus and trapped particles will then sink into the lungs, causing irritation, damaging the lung tissue and increasing the risk of disease.

Lung cancer and emphysema

Smoking cigarettes or other tobacco products is a major cause of **lung cancer** and **emphysema**.

- Lung cancer is a disease that is difficult to treat and often causes death. Tumours grow in the lungs and may spread to other parts of the body via the blood stream, as the lungs have a very good blood supply.

- Emphysema is caused by inflammation and scarring of lung tissue, and damage to the alveoli. A person with emphysema has a persistent cough and finds it difficult to breathe.

How smoking causes disease

Smoking causes lung cancer and emphysema because:

- Tobacco smoke contains many chemicals that are **carcinogens** (they cause cancer). This provides a clear link with lung cancer.

- Tobacco smoke damages the cilia that line the lungs, paralysing them and causing them to eventually die off. The lungs become clogged by mucus and irritated by the particles trapped in the mucus. This explains the development of emphysema.

- Tobacco smoke contains tar which clogs up the lungs and makes it more difficult to breathe, which again can lead to emphysema.

The vast majority of scientists are now certain that smoking is potentially very harmful to the smoker, and also to people in the vicinity who breathe in the smoke (**passive smoking**). The evidence is mainly disputed by groups with an obvious bias (e.g. studies paid for by the tobacco industry). The reasons we can be confident that smoking is linked with lung disease are:

- Many studies have shown the link – the data has been **reproducible**.

- These studies have been **peer reviewed** – other scientists have checked the methods and the results.

Attitudes to smoking

Revised

Over the last few decades, people's attitudes to smoking have changed.

- Fewer people are smoking.

- People are more aware of the effects of passive smoking.

- Smoking bans have been introduced in public places.

- Cigarette packets carry health warnings.

- The age limit for buying cigarettes has been raised from 16 to 18.

- Products and support groups exist to help people to stop smoking.

- Pregnant women now rarely smoke – they are aware of possible damage to their babies.

Examiner tip

Exam questions about 'attitudes to smoking' (and similar topics) will usually provide you with data and will not expect you to remember specific facts. But you need to be aware of the issues and be able to discuss them.

Check your understanding

Tested

24 The following table shows the death rate from lung cancer per year in men who have given up smoking cigarettes. They used to smoke 15 to 25 cigarettes per day.

Years after giving up smoking	Death rate from lung cancer per 100 000 men per year
0	120
5	55
10	35
15	25

a) What does the table show you about the benefit of giving up smoking? *(1 mark)*

b) The men in the study all smoked roughly the same number of cigarettes per day before giving up. Why is this important? *(1 mark)*

c) Name **one** disease, apart from lung cancer, that is more common in smokers than non-smokers. *(1 mark)*

d) How have people's attitudes to smoking changed over the last 15 to 20 years? *(6 marks QWC)*

Go online for answers

Online

Food and digestion

Why we need to digest food

Food provides energy for the body. In order to reach all parts, it needs to travel in the blood system. To do this, two things are necessary:

- The food must be able to get through the wall of the gut and into the blood system. Only **small molecules** can do this.
- The food needs to be in a form that is **soluble** in water, so that it can dissolve in the blood.

Digestion converts the food we eat into a form that can be transported in the blood. The complex chemicals in food are broken down into simple, soluble substances.

Substances that need to be digested

Some food chemicals (e.g. glucose, vitamins) are already simple soluble molecules and do not need to be digested. Substances that need to be digested are shown in the table.

Substance	Function in the body	Digested into
Complex carbohydrates (e.g. Starch)	Provide energy	Glucose
Proteins	Raw material for growth and repair	Amino acids
Fats	Provide energy	Fatty acids and glycerol

Food tests

Foods can be tested to see if they contain starch, glucose or protein.
The tests are all done on a **solution** of the food.

Food	Test	Positive result
Starch	Add iodine solution	Blue-black colour appears
Glucose	Add Benedict's solution. Place in a boiling water bath.	Solution goes cloudy and changes from blue to green, orange and then brick red, according to how much glucose is present.
Protein	Add an equal amount of sodium hydroxide, then a few drops of copper(II) sulphate solution.	Lilac colour appears

Using visking tubing to model the gut

Visking tubing is often used in experiments as a 'model gut'. It is **selectively permeable** which means it will let small molecules through but not large molecules. In this way, it behaves in a very similar way to the lining of the gut. The limitations of the model are:

● Visking tubing is **non-living**. The gut has mechanisms for actively extracting substances into the cells under certain circumstances, but visking tubing does not.

● The gut moves the food around by muscular contractions, but visking tubing cannot do that.

> **Examiner tip**
>
> Visking tubing is also used as a model membrane in osmosis experiments. Look carefully at the wording of the question to see if the experiment is about digestion or osmosis, and remember that it is not appropriate to use the term 'osmosis' in digestion experiments (because the substance moving will not be water).

Check your understanding

25 The visking tubing shown in the diagram represents a model of the intestine.

Starch, glucose, fats and protein were mixed in water. The mixture was poured into the visking tubing. The visking tubing was tied at the end and suspended in a test tube of water.

After 24 hours the water in the test tube was sampled.

a) Indicate with a tick (✓) or a cross (✗) in the table whether each of the food substances was present in the water or not. *(2 marks)*

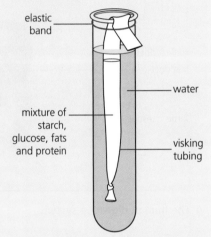

Food substance	Present in the water in the test tube after 24 hours (✓ or ✗)
Starch	
Glucose	
Fats	
Protein	

b) How would you test the water in the test tube for the presence of starch? *(2 marks)*

c) State one way in which visking tubing is a good model of the gut. *(1 mark)*

d) State one way in which the visking tubing is inaccurate as a model of the gut. *(1 mark)*

26 Lilly eats an apple and some cheese. The table shows some substances that are found in these foods, and some information about them.

Substance	Size of molecule	Solubility in water
Fructose	Small	Soluble
Protein	Large	Insoluble
Fats	Large	Insoluble
Vitamin A	Small	Soluble

a) Which substances would need to be digested in the body? Give reasons for your answer. *(3 marks)*

b) Starch is a carbohydrate which needs to be digested. What is the final product of the digestion of starch? *(1 mark)*

Go online for answers

Online

The digestive system and enzymes

The digestive system

The diagram shows the different parts of the digestive system. Each part has a specific function.

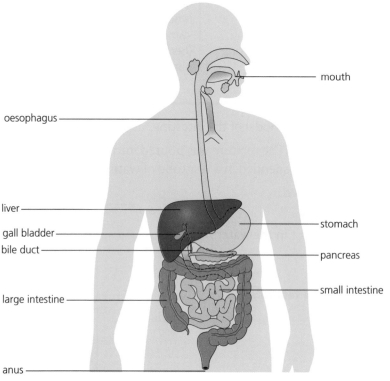

- mouth
- oesophagus
- liver
- gall bladder
- bile duct
- stomach
- pancreas
- small intestine
- large intestine
- anus

↑ **The human digestive system**

> **Examiner tip**
> You will never be asked to draw the digestive system, only to label a given diagram.

Digestive enzymes

Enzymes are very important in the digestive system. Different enzymes break down the different food groups. The types of enzymes found in the gut are:

- **Carbohydrases**: these break down carbohydrates.
- **Proteases**: these break down proteins.
- **Lipases**: these break down fats.

> **Examiner tip**
> Remember what you learnt about enzymes in the section 'Cells and cell processes' (pages 10–13). Questions on digestion may include parts on the specificity of enzymes (they only work on one type of substrate) and on the effect of high temperatures (which denature enzymes).

Functions of digestive organs

Organ	Function
Mouth	Breaks up food by chewing. Carbohydrase in saliva breaks down starch.
Stomach	Acid in the stomach kills bacteria. Stomach produces protease and lipase enzymes.
Pancreas	Produces protease, lipase and carbohydrase enzymes. These enzymes act in the small intestine.
Small intestine	Digestion is completed by carbohydrase enzymes in the small intestine. The food is absorbed in the second half of the small intestine.
Large intestine	Water from the digestive juices is re-absorbed into the blood.

Bile

Revised

Bile is a liquid that is produced in the **liver** and stored in the **gall bladder**. It is secreted down the **bile duct** into the small intestine. It contains no enzymes, but it helps in the digestion of fats. It **emulsifies** fats – breaks them into small droplets, giving a bigger surface area for lipase enzymes to act on.

Movement of food

Revised

Food is moved along the small intestine by a process called **peristalsis**. This involves the contraction of circular gut muscles behind the food, and the relaxation of the muscles in front of the food, as shown in the diagram.

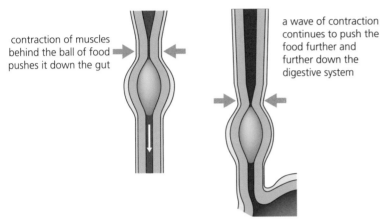

contraction of muscles behind the ball of food pushes it down the gut

a wave of contraction continues to push the food further and further down the digestive system

↑ **Peristalsis in the gut**

Check your understanding

Tested

27 a) Complete the following sentences using some of the chemicals listed here:

fatty acids   amino acids   glucose   salts

Proteins are broken down into _____. *(1 mark)*

Carbohydrates are broken down into _____. *(1 mark)*

Fats are broken down into _____ and glycerol. *(1 mark)*

b) i) Name the process by which foods are broken down. *(1 mark)*

ii) State why this process is necessary. *(1 mark)*

28 a) Complete the table below to show the actions of enzymes in different regions of the digestive system. *(3 marks)*

Region of digestive system	Enzyme	Action of enzyme
Stomach	Protease	
Small intestine		Digests starch to glucose
Pancreas	Lipase	

b) Bile is an important digestive fluid, but it contains no enzymes.

i) Where is bile produced? *(1 mark)*

ii) Where is bile stored? *(1 mark)*

iii) What is the function of bile? *(2 marks)*

Go online for answers

Online

Biodiversity

Biodiversity means the variety or number of **different species** in a given area.

Why is biodiversity important?

The more species there are in an area, the more stable the **ecosystem** is. (The ecosystem is the habitat plus all the living things in it.)

For example, if a species only has one prey species in an area, it can survive provided the numbers of prey are high enough. If, however, something happens to the prey species (e.g. disease) which reduces numbers, the predator will have no alternative food supply, and may not be able to survive in that area. If there were four or five different species that it could eat, there would always be alternatives if one of the prey populations were reduced.

Other benefits of biodiversity

● Biodiversity provides potential foods, industrial materials and new medicines for human well-being.

● Stable ecosystems help to regulate the atmosphere, water supply and nutrient cycles, and provide fertile soil.

> **Examiner tip**
>
> Be careful when defining biodiversity. It is nothing to do with the number of organisms. An area with a very large number of animals and plants could have a low biodiversity, if there were only a small number of species.

Threats to biodiversity

In order to maintain biodiversity, it is important to try to stop too many species becoming **extinct**. An **endangered species** is one whose population has dropped to such low numbers that there is a possibility that it may become extinct.

A species may be endangered in a particular country (e.g. the red squirrel in the UK) or in the whole world (e.g. the giant panda).

Reasons for a reduction in species numbers

● **Changes in land use**. Modern farming practices (e.g. large areas with just a single crop grown) and the felling of forests for farming, building or quarrying all reduce biodiversity.

● **Climate change**. Changing climate can mean that certain species can no longer survive in a given area.

● **Over-exploitation**. Over-fishing and activities such as poaching of animals (e.g. elephants for their tusks) threaten populations.

● **Introduction of 'alien' species**. Species introduced into a country can push out existing species (e.g. grey squirrels in the UK are replacing the native red squirrel).

Protecting biodiversity

Biodiversity and endangered species can be conserved and protected by legislation, for example:

- the Convention on International Trade in Endangered Species
- Sites of Special Scientific Interest, which are designated areas with protected status
- legally enforced fishing quotas.

Attempts can be made to prevent loss of biodiversity or to re-introduce species, through captive breeding programmes by zoos, establishing of national parks, setting up 'seed banks', and local biodiversity 'action plans'.

Computer programs can be used to predict the possible effects of climate change or environmental management procedures, so that future problems may be averted.

> **Examiner tip**
>
> Most of the questions on this topic will expect you to understand issues, rather than remember specific facts. They will often involve interpreting data or discussing problems.

Check your understanding

29 Read the following information about bird conservation.

In 1980 the kingfisher was an endangered species in a part of South Wales. Conservation workers set up nest places and perches near rivers. They also helped to reduce river pollution.

In 2006 there were 6000 birds, five times more than in 1980.

In the north of England, the sea eagle had died out by 1918. Conservationists introduced a few eagles from another country in 1950 and breeding was very successful.

↑ Kingfisher

Using this information only:

a) i) Why is it very important for kingfishers that their river water is not polluted? *(1 mark)*

   ii) Give **one** example of conservation work, other than reducing pollution, which helped kingfishers. *(1 mark)*

   iii) How many kingfishers were there in 1980? Show your working. *(1 mark)*

b) i) After sea eagles had disappeared, how long was it before conservation work started? *(1 mark)*

   ii) What evidence is there that the number of sea eagles has increased because of conservation? *(1 mark)*

Go online for answers

Measuring biodiversity

Sampling

When investigating biodiversity, the area studied is usually large. It is not practical to find and record all the living things in such a large space, so scientists have to **sample** the area. This means looking closely at a smaller area, and then calculating the numbers in the larger area mathematically.

For samples to be useful, the following points must be considered:

● The sample area must be **typical** of the whole area.

● The bigger the sample area is, the better, as small areas are less likely to be typical.

● The method of sampling **must not affect the results** (e.g. with some animals the presence of humans might scare them away).

Samples cannot be absolutely accurate, so scientists often use **statistical analysis** which takes account of sample size when drawing conclusions.

Quadrats

A **quadrat** is a square frame used to sample a measured area. They are placed **randomly** in the area to be studied. The individuals of different species in each quadrat are then counted and recorded. An example calculation of total numbers in an area follows:

Total area studied = $1000\,m^2$

Area of quadrat = $1\,m^2$

Number of quadrats = 50

Total sample area = $50\,m^2$

Number of species X recorded in quadrats = 133

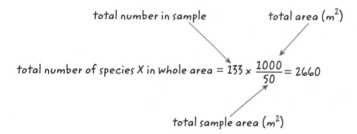

It is important that the quadrats are placed randomly so that the person placing them does not introduce any **bias** into the results. This can be done by marking out the area as a numbered grid, then using a random number generator to decide which grid squares to place the quadrats in.

> **Examiner tip**
>
> When answering questions on quadrats, always describe the numbered grid system. It might be easier to just drop the quadrat without looking, but this is not a truly random method.

A **transect** is a set of samples taken down a set line, usually marked by a chain or tape. Samples are taken at **measured intervals** (e.g. every metre) and the species under the sampling point are recorded.

Transects are usually used to measure how populations change along some sort of gradient, for example between a light and a shaded area of woodland, or up a shore from the low tide mark to the high tide mark.

30 David was studying the population of snails in a field. The total area of the field was 2000 m². He chose a spot near the middle of the field to place a quadrat. The quadrat is shown below.

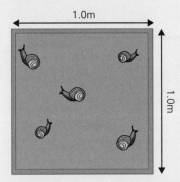

1.0m

1.0m

a) Estimate the population of snails that would be found in the whole of the 2000 m² field. Show your working. *(4 marks)*

b) Suggest **two** reasons why this estimate is likely to be inaccurate. Explain your answers. *(2 marks)*

31 Beth was trying to measure the population of snakes in a wood. The wood covered an area of 100 000 m². She carefully measured an area of 1000 m², and systematically searched it for snakes. In this area, Beth found two snakes. From this data, she estimated what the population of snakes in the whole wood would be.

a) Estimate the population of snakes in the wood. Show your working. *(2 marks)*

b) This estimate is likely to be inaccurate. The following could be possible explanations for this inaccuracy. For each, state whether it is a **possible** explanation (**true**) or not (**false**). *(2 marks)*

   A   The sample area was not big enough.

   B   The snakes may not be evenly distributed in the wood.

   C   Some snakes may have moved out of the area when they detected Beth coming.

   D   Snakes are camouflaged and Beth may have missed some.

Biological control

What is biological control?

Biological control is the use of living organisms to control the population of a pest species. The biological **control agents** are usually predators, parasites or micro-organisms that cause death by disease. Biological control is an alternative to **chemical control**, which is the use of chemical pesticides to kill pests.

The biological control agent is introduced into the habitat to reduce a pest problem, and so it is always a species that is not already present in the environment. It is very often a species from a different country. Such species are called **alien species**.

Advantages of biological control

- No chemicals are used that may persist in the ground or on a crop and so enter the human food chain.
- If carefully selected, a biological control agent will attack just the pest species. Many chemical pesticides affect many species besides the pest (e.g. some insecticides kill a wide range of insects).
- Biological control usually reduces the pest population to manageable levels, rather than wiping it out completely. This makes for a more stable ecosystem.

Disadvantages of biological control

- It is more complicated to operate than chemical control.
- It is difficult to use outdoors (because containing the agent is difficult) and so is mostly restricted to greenhouse crops.
- It is more expensive than chemical control (due to its complicated nature).
- The biological control agent may cause other problems in the ecosystem.

↑ **Ladybirds are a form of biological control in the garden and can be used in greenhouses. They eat greenfly, which feed on plants**

Problems with alien species

Revised

Species are sometimes introduced into a country or area where they do not naturally occur. This may be done deliberately (as with biological control agents) or accidentally. The country where the alien species has been introduced may have no natural predators, and the new species may become **invasive**. Invasive species may grow in numbers faster than native species and upset the natural ecosystem. Native species may not be able to compete.

Examiner tip

You won't be expected to know about any particular alien species (although it is useful to study an example of a problem with an alien species in order to understand the principles). Exam questions on this topic usually give you the information you need, and it is important to read the question carefully.

Changes in biological control

Revised

Biological control methods have become more sophisticated over the years. Many of the problems (such as those with invasive species) happened in the early stages. Detailed research and scientifically based trials mean that much more is known about the control agents now, and this has reduced problems.

Check your understanding

Tested

32 Floating pennywort is an alien plant species in Britain. It grows in slow-flowing waterways such as canals and lakes, where it forms dense mats that grow at the rate of 20 cm² a day. Floating pennywort out-competes native plants, reduces the oxygen content of water and has a damaging effect on flood control.

a) What is meant by an alien species? *(1 mark)*

b) State **one** harmful effect that floating pennywort could have on native wildlife. *(1 mark)*

c) In Florida the southern army worm is known to eat floating pennywort and in Argentina there is a weevil (an insect) that only eats floating pennywort. What advice would you give the Environment Agency about the dangers of introducing these organisms into Britain as methods of biological control against floating pennywort? *(2 marks)*

33 Japanese knotweed is a troublesome invasive weed species in Britain. It has been suggested that an insect species from Japan may be able to control it. Explain the possible problems that scientists should consider before using this insect. *(6 marks QWC)*

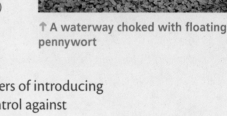
↑ A waterway choked with floating pennywort

Go online for answers

Online

The capture–recapture technique

The technique

The **capture–recapture technique** is used to estimate the population of an animal species. It is carried out as follows:

1 A number of individuals of a particular species are captured.

2 These animals are marked in some way (e.g. with a spot of paint).

3 They are released back into the wild.

4 Later, another sample of the species is captured.

The proportion of marked individuals in the second sample is estimated to be the same as the proportion of those marked initially in the total population.

The population can therefore be estimated using the equation:

$$N = \frac{MC}{R}$$

where:

N = estimate of total population size

M = total number of animals captured and marked on the first visit

C = total number of animals captured on the second visit

R = number of animals captured on the first visit that were then recaptured on the second visit

> **Examiner tip**
>
> You will not be expected to remember the equation for estimating the population using this technique, but you will be expected to use it correctly.

↑ **A marked woodlouse. It is important that the paint spot is not too big or it might make the woodlouse easier for the person collecting woodlice (or predators) to spot**

Using the technique

For the population estimate to be accurate, certain conditions must apply:

● Sufficient time has elapsed between the two samples for the marked individuals to mix with the rest of the population.

● There is no large-scale movement of animals into or out of the area in the time between the two samples.

● The marking does not affect the survival chances of the animal (e.g. by making it easier for a predator to see it).

● The marking does not affect the chances of recapture by making the marked individuals more 'noticeable' to the collector.

Example

200 woodlice were captured in a garden and marked with paint. They were released, and three weeks later another sample, this time of 100 woodlice, was taken. Of the 100 captured, 3 were marked with paint.

To calculate the number of woodlice in the garden, we use the equation:

$$N = \frac{MC}{R}$$

$$N = \frac{200 \times 100}{3} = \frac{20\,000}{3} = 6666.66 = 6667$$

> **Examiner tip**
>
> The answer is rounded up, because you cannot have 0.66 of a woodlouse!

Check your understanding

34 Scientists were studying the number of centipedes in a wooded area. Centipedes are active invertebrates that feed on other invertebrates in leaf litter. Their predators include birds and toads. The scientists captured 100 centipedes and marked them with green paint. A week later, they returned to the area and captured 60 centipedes. Of these, 5 were marked with green paint.

↑ A centipede

a) Using the formula given on this spread, calculate the total number of centipedes in the area. (2 marks)

b) Suggest why the scientists used green paint rather than white. (2 marks)

c) The scientists did a further study, on snails. This time, they left a month between samples. Suggest a reason for this. (2 marks)

Go online for answers

Atomic structure

Review of atomic structure

Over many years, the idea of atomic structure has changed through observations and the gathering of experimental evidence.

● Atoms consist of a central **nucleus** surrounded by one or more **shells** of **electrons**.

● The nucleus consists of two types of particle, **protons** and **neutrons**.

● The protons and neutrons are very small. They have a **relative mass** of 1. The relative mass of an electron is so small it is negligible.

Charges in the nucleus

● A proton has a positive charge, an electron has a negative charge, and neutrons have no charge.

● Overall, the atom has no electrical charge, because the number of electrons in the shells is equal to the number of protons in the nucleus.

Particle	Relative mass	Relative charge
Proton	1	+1
Neutron	1	0
Electron	Negligible	−1

Atomic number and mass number

● The number of protons in an atom is its **proton number** or **atomic number**.

● The number of nucleons (protons + neutrons) is the **mass number**.

● Therefore, the number of neutrons is (mass number − proton number).

Sometimes the chemical symbol for an element is written in a way that shows the atomic number and the mass number. An example (carbon) is given below.

mass number ⟶ 12
atomic number ⟶ 6 C

↑ **Carbon has 6 protons and 6 neutrons (i.e. 12 nucleons)**

> **Examiner tip**
>
> Chemistry exam papers always have a copy of the Periodic Table at the back, which shows the mass number and atomic number of each element. This information can be useful for answering some questions.

> **Examiner tip**
>
> In an exam question you may be asked about the number of neutrons or electrons in an atom. You need to remember that the number of electrons is the same as the number of protons (i.e. the atomic number), and the number of neutrons is the mass number minus the atomic number.

Isotopes

Different elements have different atomic (proton) numbers: no two elements have the same number of protons. However, the number of neutrons in the nucleus is not fixed. Some atoms of the same element have different numbers of neutrons, and so different mass numbers. These different forms of the same element are called **isotopes**.

The most common form of carbon has 6 protons and 6 neutrons, and so has a mass number of 12. There is another isotope of carbon which has 6 protons and 8 neutrons:

$$^{14}_{6}C$$

↑ The carbon-14 isotope has a mass number of 14

Check your understanding

1   This is the symbol for aluminium.

$$^{27}_{13}Al$$

   a) What is the atomic number of aluminium?   (1 mark)

   b) What is the mass number of aluminium?   (1 mark)

   c) How many neutrons would be found in the aluminium atom's nucleus?   (1 mark)

   d) What is the total number of electrons in an aluminium atom? Explain how you reached your answer.   (2 marks)

2   The diagram below shows an atom of lithium.

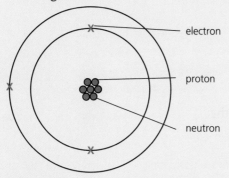

↑ Lithium

   a) What is the atomic number of lithium?   (1 mark)

   b) What is the mass number of lithium?   (1 mark)

   c) The relative mass of a proton is 1. What is the relative mass of a neutron?   (1 mark)

   d) This form of lithium has 4 neutrons. Another form has only 3 neutrons. What name is given to these different forms of the same atom?   (1 mark)

Go online for answers

Atoms and the Periodic Table

Masses of atoms and molecules

Scientists express the mass of an atom relative to the mass of the carbon atom, ^{12}C. The mass of ^{12}C is given as 12, its mass number. The mass of another atom is compared with 1/12 of the mass of a carbon-12 atom. This called its **relative atomic mass**, symbol A_r.

When atoms form molecules, the relative mass of the molecule can be calculated by adding together the relative atomic masses of the atoms that make it up. This is called the **relative molecular mass**, symbol M_r. Relative molecular mass is known as **relative formula mass** when talking about ionic compounds.

For example, lead sulfate has the formula $PbSO_4$. It contains 1 atom of lead, 1 atom of sulfur, and 4 atoms of oxygen. The A_r of these atoms are:

    lead (Pb) = 207

    sulfur (S) = 32

    oxygen (O) = 16

So the M_r of lead sulfate = 207 + 32 + (4 × 16) = 303

Electronic structure

The electrons in an atom are at different **energy levels** around the nucleus. The energy levels are sometimes called **shells** or **orbits**. Each shell can contain up to a maximum number of electrons:

● the first shell can contain up to 2 electrons

● shells 2 and 3 can contain up to 8 electrons.

Electrons don't occupy an outer shell unless the inner shells are full.

Nitrogen has an atomic number of 7. From this, we can work out its **electronic structure**, which is shown in the diagram below. We know the atom has 7 protons and so must have 7 electrons.

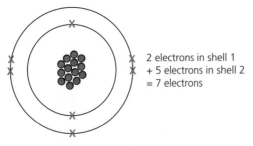

    2 electrons in shell 1
    + 5 electrons in shell 2
    = 7 electrons

↑ **Electronic structure of nitrogen**

The electronic structure is written as the number of electrons in each shell, separated by a comma. For example, the electronic structure of nitrogen is 2,5. The electronic structure of potassium is 2,8,8,1.

Electron configuration is an alternative term for electronic structure.

Electronic structure and the Periodic Table

The electronic structure of an element can be worked out from its position in the Periodic Table.

- The **group** number gives the number of electrons in the outer shell. The exception to this is Group 0, which indicates that the outer shell is full (however many electrons it can contain).

- The **period** indicates how many shells of electrons the atom has.

Examiner tip

You will only be asked about the electronic structure of the first 20 elements in the Periodic Table. You don't need to learn the structure, because you can work it out from the atomic number, which you can find in the Periodic Table.

Examiner tip

Remember that the columns in the Periodic Table are called groups, and the rows are called periods.

Check your understanding

3 The table shows the relative atomic masses (A_r) of some elements.

Element	Relative atomic mass (A_r)
Hydrogen	1.0
Carbon	12.0
Oxygen	16.0
Sodium	23.0
Sulfur	32.0
Chlorine	35.5
Calcium	40.0

Use this information to calculate the relative molecular masses (M_r) of the following substances:

a) water, H_2O (1 mark)

b) calcium chloride, $CaCl_2$ (1 mark)

c) sulfuric acid, H_2SO_4 (1 mark)

d) sodium carbonate, Na_2CO_3 (1 mark)

4 Draw **three** diagrams to show the electronic structure of the following three atoms.   (3 marks)

$^{11}_{5}B$ $^{24}_{12}Mg$ $^{20}_{10}Ne$
boron   magnesium   neon

The alkali metals

The **alkali metals** are the reactive elements in Group 1 of the Periodic Table: lithium (Li), sodium (Na), potassium (K), rubidium (Rb), caesium (Cs) and francium (Fr).

1	2											3	4	5	6	7	0
							H										He
Li	Be											B	C	N	O	F	Ne
Na	Mg											Al	Si	P	S	Cl	Ar
K	Ca	Sc	Ti	V	Cr	Mn	Fe	Co	Ni	Cu	Zn	Ga	Ge	As	Se	Br	Kr
Rb	Sr	Y	Zr	Nb	Mo	Tc	Ru	Rh	Pd	Ag	Cd	In	Sn	Sb	Te	I	Xe
Cs	Ba	La	Hf	Ta	W	Re	Os	Ir	Pt	Au	Hg	Tl	Pb	Bi	Po	At	Rn
Fr	Ra	Ac															

↑ **Group 1 of the Periodic Table**

Reactions with oxygen — Revised

The alkali metals are soft, shiny metals that react immediately on contact with the oxygen in air – they tarnish, or corrode, forming a layer of the metal oxide on the surface. They need to be stored under oil. They burn readily in oxygen. For example:

lithium + oxygen ⟶ lithium oxide

$$4Li(s) + O_2(g) \longrightarrow 2Li_2O(s)$$

The other alkali metals react in a similar way, and the reactions become **progressively more violent down the group**.

Reactions with water — Revised

The alkali metals react vigorously with water. Lithium fizzes on contact with water, forming the alkali lithium hydroxide and bubbles of hydrogen gas.

lithium + water ⟶ lithium hydroxide + hydrogen

$$2Li(s) + 2H_2O(l) \longrightarrow 2LiOH(aq) + H_2(g)$$

The other alkali metals react in a similar way, and again the reactions become **progressively more violent down the group**. Sodium fizzes violently. Potassium creates so much heat as it reacts with water that it ignites the hydrogen, producing a lilac flame. The other alkali metals react so violently that it is not safe to carry out these reactions in school.

↑ **Lithium reacting with water**

Reactions with halogens — Revised

The **halogens** is the name given to the elements in Group 7 of the Periodic Table, including chlorine, Cl, and bromine, Br.

Lithium reacts (burns) readily in chlorine gas, producing the salt lithium chloride, LiCl:

lithium + chlorine ⟶ lithium chloride

$$2Li(s) + Cl_2(g) \longrightarrow 2LiCl(s)$$

Lithium reacts with bromine in a similar way, forming lithium bromide.

The other alkali metals react similarly, and again the reactions become **progressively more violent down the group**.

The reactions of the alkali metals with oxygen, with water and with the halogens show us that the **reactivity** of the alkali metals **increases down the group**. The least reactive alkali metal is lithium, and the most reactive is francium. Potassium is the most reactive alkali metal allowed in schools.

Examiner tip

Questions about reactions of the alkali metals often ask for safety advice (as in Question **7** below), because the reactions are sometimes quite violent. Good general advice is to think about using: safety glasses/goggles, safety screens, only a small piece of the metal, and tongs or tweezers.

Flame tests

Revised

Alkali metals present in compounds such as lithium chloride, sodium bromide or potassium sulfate, can be identified by strongly heating a sample in a roaring Bunsen burner flame and noting the colour observed.

● Lithium compounds produce a red coloured flame.

● Sodium compounds produce an yellow-orange coloured flame.

● Potassium compounds produce a lilac coloured flame.

← Lithium compounds burn red in a Bunsen flame

Check your understanding

Tested

5 The table below shows some physical properties of Group 1 elements.

Element	Melting point (°C)	Boiling point (°C)	Density (g/cm³)	Electrical conductivity
Lithium	180	1340	0.50	Good
Sodium	98	880	0.97	Good
Potassium	63	766	0.86	Good
Rubidium	39	686	1.50	Good
Caesium	29	669	1.90	Good

Use the information in the table above to answer parts (a)–(c).

a) State **one** property of Group 1 elements which is:

i) common to all metals *(1 mark)*

ii) not common to all metals. *(1 mark)*

b) Francium lies below caesium in Group 1. Predict the approximate value for the melting point of francium. Give the reason for your choice of value. *(2 marks)*

c) Describe the general trend in the density of Group 1 metals going down the group. *(1 mark)*

6 a) When a freshly cut piece of potassium is exposed to air, its cut surface immediately reacts with oxygen, O_2, forming potassium oxide. Write a balanced symbol equation for this reaction. *(3 marks)*

b) State how this change is normally prevented when storing potassium in the laboratory. *(1 mark)*

c) A flame test can be used to identify the potassium in potassium iodide. State what you would expect to see. *(1 mark)*

7 A technician found that the labels had come off bottles containing the alkali metals lithium, sodium and potassium. Describe a simple test she could carry out in order to identify the metals. Give a safety precaution she must take and describe the expected observations for each metal. *(4 marks)*

Go online for answers

Online

The halogens

The **halogens** are the reactive elements in Group 7 of the Periodic Table: fluorine (F), chlorine (Cl), bromine (Br), iodine (I), and astatine (At).

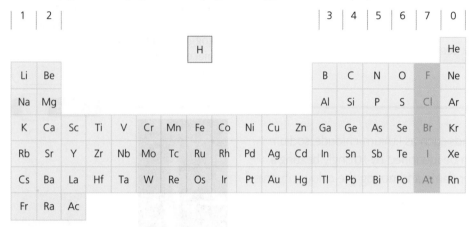

↑ **Group 7 of the Periodic Table**

Reactions with iron
Revised

The table summarises the reactions of the halogens with iron.

Halogen	Reaction with iron wool	Product
Fluorine	Cold iron wool bursts into flame as fluorine gas flows over it.	Iron(III) fluoride, FeF_3
Chlorine	Hot iron wool glows brightly when chlorine gas flows over it.	Iron(III) chloride, $FeCl_3$
Bromine	Hot iron wool glows, but less brightly, when bromine vapour flows over it.	Iron(III) bromide, $FeBr_3$
Iodine	Hot iron wool shows a faint red glow when iodine vapour flows over it.	Iron(III) iodide, FeI_3

Fluorine is a **very** reactive gas that cannot be used in school.

The reaction equation of fluorine with iron is:

$$\text{iron} + \text{fluorine} \longrightarrow \text{iron(III) fluoride}$$
$$2Fe(s) + 3F_2(g) \longrightarrow 2FeF_3(s)$$

The other halogens follow a similar equation pattern.

The halogens get **progressively less reactive down the group**.

Displacement reactions
Revised

A more reactive halogen can **displace** a less reactive halogen from a solution of its salt. For example chlorine, the second most reactive halogen, will displace both bromine and iodine from solutions of bromides and iodides.

$$\text{chlorine} + \text{sodium bromide} \longrightarrow \text{bromine} + \text{sodium chloride}$$
$$Cl_2(g) + 2NaBr(aq) \longrightarrow Br_2(l) + 2NaCl(aq)$$

In the same way, bromine, which is more reactive than iodine, displaces iodine from iodide solutions.

Silver nitrate test

Halide ions can be identified by their reactions with aqueous silver nitrate. Chloride, bromide and iodide ions in solution combine with the silver ions in silver nitrate to form insoluble **precipitates** of:

● white silver chloride

● cream silver bromide

● yellow silver iodide.

These reactions form the basis of identifying each **halide** salt.

Silver nitrate contains the silver ion, Ag^+, and the nitrate ion, NO_3^-. Sodium chloride contains the sodium ion, Na^+, and the chloride ion, Cl^-. The important reaction that takes place when the two solutions react is the one between the silver ions and the chloride ions:

$$Ag^+(aq) + Cl^-(aq) \longrightarrow AgCl(s)$$

Silver chloride is a white solid and precipitates out of solution. The other ions stay in solution.

> **Examiner tip**
>
> A table of common ions is always given in Chemistry exam papers. You do not need to learn them. You must however practise identifying the ions produced when ionic compounds dissolve in water. Remember to always write the charge as a superscript by the element symbols.

Check your understanding

8 Group 7 of the Periodic Table is shown. E represents a Group 7 element. E is not the symbol of the element.

Group 7
Fluorine
Chlorine
Bromine
E
Astatine

a) Name element E. *(1 mark)*

b) Give the number of electrons in the outer orbit (shell) of an atom of fluorine. *(1 mark)*

c) Choose from the list below the name by which Group 7 elements are also known. *(1 mark)*

alkali metals   halogens   noble gases   transition metals

9 a) i) A series of experiments was carried out to investigate the displacement reactions of Group 7 elements (halogens). Each halogen was added to a solution containing a different halide ion. Complete the table by entering a **tick** in a box where you would expect a displacement reaction to occur, or a **cross** where you would expect no reaction. Two have been done for you. *(2 marks)*

Halogen	Solution of halide ion		
	Sodium chloride	Sodium bromide	Sodium iodide
Bromine, Br_2	✗		✓
Chlorine, Cl_2			
Iodine, I_2			

ii) Write a balanced symbol equation for the reaction between bromine, Br_2, and sodium iodide solution, NaI. *(2 marks)*

b) Sodium iodide is used in medicine to treat thyroid disorders. A pupil was asked to identify the presence of sodium ions and iodide ions in a sample of sodium iodide. State the result the pupil should expect if:

i) a flame test was carried out on the sample *(1 mark)*

ii) silver nitrate solution was added to a solution of the sample. *(1 mark)*

Go online for answers

Chemical bonding 1

Metallic bonding

All solid metals have a structure consisting of a **lattice** (regular repeating structure) of positive ions, throughout which a 'sea' of free electrons moves, creating **metallic bonds**. The free electrons are able to move easily throughout the structure.

Explaining physical properties

The lattice/free electron model explains:

- the high **electrical conductivity** of metals. The sea of free electrons moves easily throughout the structure of the metal. Electrons carry a negative charge, so electric current (a flow of charge) can pass easily through the structure when there is an applied voltage.

- the high **thermal conductivity** of metals. The positive ions are close together and bonded strongly by metallic bonds. The structure can easily pass the vibration of hot ions from one ion to the next ion; also the free electrons can move faster as they are heated and transfer the heat from hot to cold throughout the structure.

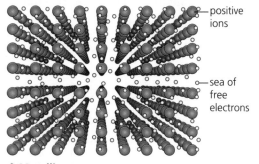
positive ions

sea of free electrons

↑ **Metallic structure**

Ionic bonding

Sodium chloride is a good example of an **ionic compound**. An atom of sodium has the electronic structure 2,8,1. An atom of chlorine has the electronic structure 2,8,7. When sodium reacts with chlorine to make sodium chloride, a sodium atom loses its outermost electron, and a chlorine atom gains an electron. Both form ions with the stable electronic structure of a noble gas.

The sodium atom becomes a positively charged sodium ion, Na^+ (because it has lost an electron), and the chlorine atom becomes a negatively charged chloride ion, Cl^- (because it has gained an electron).

> **Examiner tip**
>
> In common chemical bonding questions you are given the physical properties of a selection of substances, and are asked to identify the substances. Spend time in the exam studying the properties carefully.

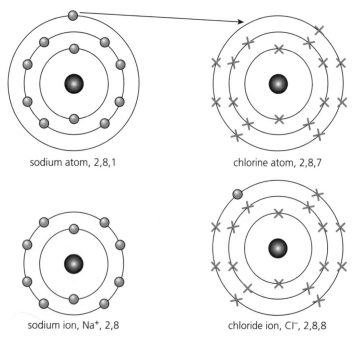

sodium atom, 2,8,1   chlorine atom, 2,8,7

sodium ion, Na^+, 2,8   chloride ion, Cl^-, 2,8,8

↑ **Formation of positive and negative ions by electron transfer**

The salt, sodium chloride, is electrically neutral, so there must be equal numbers of sodium ions and chloride ions. The total positive charges cancel out the total negative charges.

Positive charges attract negative charges strongly (through electrostatic attraction), so the ions are held together in a regular three-dimensional **lattice** (regular repeating structure) by these strong electrostatic forces.

Explaining physical properties

The ionic lattice model explains:

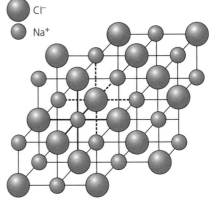

- the **high melting points** of ionic compounds. The positive and negative ions have very strong attractive electrostatic forces between them, which need a lot of energy (from heating) to overcome them.

- why solid ionic compounds do not conduct electricity. The positive and negative ions are held in fixed positions within their lattice and are not free to move. As there are no moving charged particles, there will be no electrical conduction.

- why, when molten or dissolved in water, ionic compounds do conduct electricity. The lattice breaks down on melting or dissolving, and the ions are free to move and create an electrical current.

↑ **Sodium chloride ionic lattice**

- the **brittleness** of ionic substances. If a stress force is applied to an ionic solid (a crystal), this shifts the ion layers slightly and the layers will tend to jump over each other. Ions of the same charge are then brought side by side and so repel each other. The crystal fractures.

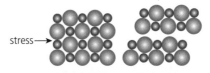

↑ **Sodium chloride is brittle**

Check your understanding
Tested

10 a) Complete the following sentence by choosing the correct word.

Sodium chloride conducts electricity when in solution due to it being a **(metallic/ionic/covalent)** compound. *(1 mark)*

b) The diagram shows the structure of a metal.

i) Use the diagram to explain why metals are good conductors of electricity. *(1 mark)*

ii) State **one** property of a metal that can be explained by the fact that the ions can be forced over each other. *(1 mark)*

+ = positive ion

− = free electron

11 The table shows the properties of four substances A–D.

Substance	Melting point (°C)	Boiling point (°C)	State at 20 °C	Soluble in water?	Conducts electricity?
A	842	1484	Solid	No	Yes
B	615	876	Solid	Yes	Only when molten/ in solution
C	−210	−196	Gas	Yes	No
D	650	1091	Solid	No	Yes

a) State which **two** of the substances, A–D, are metals and give one reason for your choice. *(2 marks)*

b) State which **one** of the substances, A–D, is an ionic compound and give one reason for your choice. *(2 marks)*

Go online for answers
Online

Chemical bonding 2

Simple molecular bonding

- Molecules are formed from atoms when they share electrons, making a **covalent bond**.
- Each atom shares enough electrons to fill its outer electron shell.
- **Dot and cross diagrams** can be used to show how covalent bonds are formed.
- Covalent bonds can also be represented by a line between two atoms in a **structural formula**.
- Some atoms can form **double covalent bonds** where each atom shares four electrons (in two pairs). This occurs in carbon dioxide.

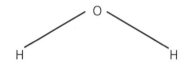

↑ Dot and cross diagram for hydrogen and oxygen forming water

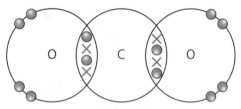

↑ Dot and cross diagram for carbon and oxygen forming carbon dioxide

↑ Structural formula of water

Explaining physical properties

- Covalent bonds between atoms in a molecule are very strong.
- Only very weak forces exist between different molecules – each molecule is overall electrically neutral.
- Solid covalent substances have **low melting points**, as very little energy is required to separate the molecules and turn the solid to a liquid. Many covalent compounds are liquids or gases at room temperature.

Giant covalent substances

- Diamond and graphite consist of carbon atoms and are **giant covalent structures**.
- They have **high melting points**, because all the atoms are held together by strong covalent bonds.
- Carbon has four outer electrons; it needs to share four other electrons to get a complete outer electron shell.

In diamond, each carbon atom is connected to **four** other carbon atoms by strong covalent bonds, forming a tetrahedral-shaped structure.

In graphite, layers of carbon atoms are arranged in hexagonal rings. Each carbon atom forms strong covalent bonds with **three** others in the same layer. The fourth electron from each atom joins a mobile system of electrons between the layers. These free electrons form bonds **between** the layers that are quite weak and allow the layers to slide over one another.

Explaining physical properties

In diamond, all four of the outer electrons are involved in covalent bonding and a rigid giant covalent structure of carbon atoms is formed. This gives diamond its extreme **hardness** and high melting point, as a lot of energy is required to break down the lattice. There are no free electrons to conduct electricity.

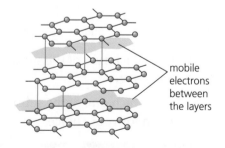

↑ The structure of diamond

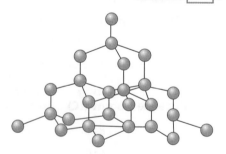

mobile electrons between the layers

↑ The structure of graphite

In graphite, the bonds between the layers are very weak, so it has a 'slippery' feel and good **lubricating** properties. The strong covalent bonds within the layers mean that the melting point is high. The mobile electrons allow graphite to conduct electricity quite well along the layers, but it does not conduct electricity across the layers.

Carbon nanotubes
Revised

Carbon **nanotubes** are another physical form of carbon. They are molecular-scale tubes of rolled-up graphite layers, about 10 000 times thinner than a human hair. They are stiffer and stronger than steel, and they can conduct electricity better than copper.

Explaining physical properties

The covalently bonded hexagonal carbon sheets make carbon nanotubes incredibly strong. The free electrons give them a high electrical conductivity.

> **Examiner tip**
>
> Some exam questions are very specific about the information that you should use to complete your answer. For example, Question **13** below says that you should only use the information from the table. You will not get credit for using other information, even though it may be correct.

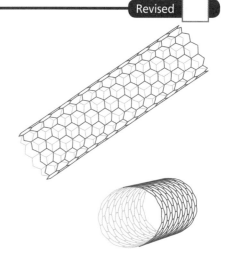

↑ Carbon nanotubes

Check your understanding
Tested

12 The following diagrams, A, B and C, show the structures of methane, graphite and diamond, but not necessarily in that order. State the correct name of each. *(2 marks)*

A 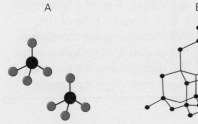   B 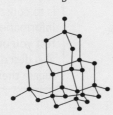   C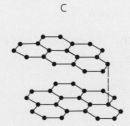

13 The table below gives some properties of four different substances, A, B, C and D. These four substances are diamond, iron, methane and sodium chloride, but not necessarily in that order.

Substance	Melting point (°C)	Boiling point (°C)	Conducts electricity	Conducts heat	Density (g/cm³)
A	801	1465	Yes when molten	No	2.16
B	1540	2750	Yes	Yes	7.9
C	3800	4800	No	No	3.5
D	−182	−162	No	No	0.47

Use only the information in the table to identify each of the following substances and to give a reason for your choice.

a) Diamond *(2 marks)*

b) Methane *(2 marks)*

Go online for answers
Online

Smart materials

Smart materials have properties which change reversibly with a change in their surroundings.

Smart pigments

Pigments are used in paints and dyes.

Thermochromic pigments change colour at a specific temperature. Their uses include:

- mugs that change colour when they have hot liquids in them
- battery power indicators
- T-shirts that change colour depending on body temperature.

Photochromic pigments change colour with light intensity. Their uses include:

- T-shirt design
- photochromic (self-darkening) lenses in glasses.

Shape-memory materials

Shape-memory polymers are plastics that, after deformation, can regain their original shape when they are heated. This property is called **shape retention**. Their uses include:

- sealing around window frames
- sportswear such as helmets and gum-shields.

Shape-memory alloys are metal alloys that regain their original shape when they are heated. Their uses include:

- surgical plates for joining bone fractures
- surgical wires for replacing tendons
- thermostats for electrical devices
- applications in the aeronautical industry, for example shape-memory alloy wires that can be heated by an electric current and made to operate wing-flaps
- deformable spectacle frames.

Examiner tip

Questions on smart materials usually ask you to match a material to its special property or to an application. A good way to revise is to construct a table of this information and ask someone to test you on it. Make sure you can also describe how the materials regain their original properties.

⬆ **Deformable spectacles that regain their shape in the warmth of the hand**

Hydrogels are polymers that can absorb or expel water and swell or shrink (up to 1000 times their volume). Small changes in the **stimulus** – either temperature or pH – control the amount of swelling (water absorbed) or shrinking (water expelled). Their uses include:

- underground water cut-off in the oil industry (the volume of gel is pH-controlled)
- artificial muscles (hydrogels are sometimes more effective than shape-memory alloys)
- buildings threatened by forest fires (hydrogels can be more effective than fire-fighting foam).

Check your understanding

Tested

14 Smart materials are materials whose properties change with changes in their surroundings. The following boxes show the names of some types of smart material and their special properties.

a) Link each smart material to its special property. One has already been done for you. *(2 marks)*

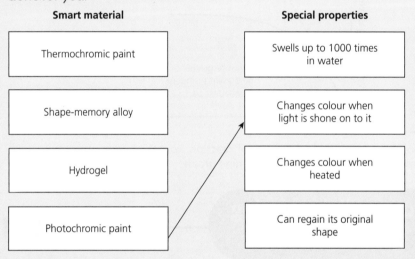

Smart material	Special properties
Thermochromic paint	Swells up to 1000 times in water
Shape-memory alloy	Changes colour when light is shone on to it
Hydrogel	Changes colour when heated
Photochromic paint	Can regain its original shape

b) From the boxes above, suggest a smart material that could be used in making:

  i) spectacle frames

  ii) nappies. *(2 marks)*

15 a) Two types of smart material are thermochromic paints and photochromic paints. Give **one** similarity and **one** difference between the properties of these materials. *(2 marks)*

b) 'Magic snow' is a special type of smart material that is capable of absorbing many times its own weight in water. It swells rapidly when it gets wet to form a snow-like mass. Name the type of smart material present in 'magic snow'. *(1 mark)*

c) One medical use of a particular smart material is as an implant under the skin that slowly releases medication. Suggest **one** reason why some scientists are concerned about this use. *(1 mark)*

Go online for answers

Online

Rate of chemical change 1

Measuring the rate of a reaction
Revised ☐

The **rate of a reaction** means how much product (usually by mass or volume) is produced in a set time (usually per second). A graph of amount of product against time allows us to determine the rate of the reaction – the gradient (slope) of the graph tells us how much product is being produced per unit time.

There are three simple ways of measuring rates of reaction in a school laboratory.

Measuring the volume of gas produced
Revised ☐

This can be done by displacing water from a graduated tube or by collecting the gas directly using a gas syringe. The volume of gas produced will increase with time, up to a maximum volume.

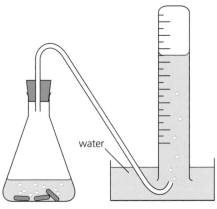

⬆ **A method of capturing gas produced**

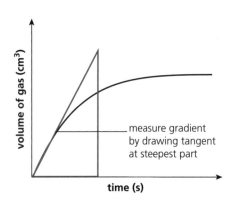

⬆ **How to find the rate of reaction from the gradient of the volume–time graph**

Measuring the amount of light passing through
Revised ☐

Some reactions produce a solid **precipitate**. If light is shone through the reaction, as more and more precipitate forms the light intensity passing through the reaction will decrease. This can be measured using a light sensor.

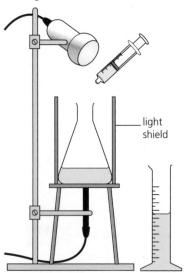

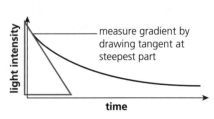

⬆ **Measuring the intensity of light passing through a reaction vessel; and finding the rate of reaction from the intensity–time graph**

Measuring the change in mass

An electronic balance can be used to measure the overall mass of a reaction. If gas is produced as one of the reaction products, then the overall mass of the reaction will decrease with time as the gas escapes.

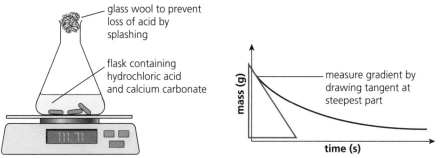

- glass wool to prevent loss of acid by splashing
- flask containing hydrochloric acid and calcium carbonate

mass (g)

measure gradient by drawing tangent at steepest part

time (s)

↑ **Measuring the mass of a reaction; and finding the rate of reaction from the gradient of the mass–time graph**

> **Examiner tip**
>
> Rate of reaction questions frequently involve plotting/sketching and analysing graphs. Make sure that you read the graph axes carefully – check the units and the scale. If you have to give a value from the graph in the exam, use a ruler and a sharp pencil to read off values from the axes.

Check your understanding

16 A student studied the rate of a reaction between hydrochloric acid and marble chips. He added excess acid to different amounts of marble chips and recorded the volume of gas produced every minute. The results are shown in the graph. Use the graph to answer the following questions.

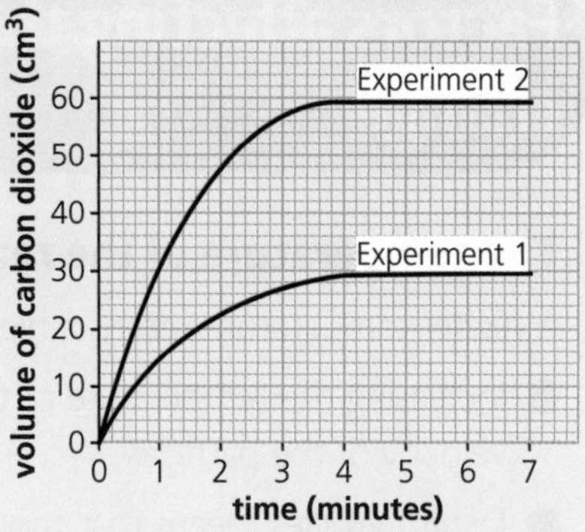

a) Give:

  i) the volume of gas produced after 1 minute in Experiment 2 *(1 mark)*

  ii) the time taken for the reaction to end in Experiment 1. *(1 mark)*

b) 0.2 g of marble chips were used in Experiment 1. Give the mass of marble chips used in Experiment 2. *(1 mark)*

c) The reaction in Experiment 2 was faster than that in Experiment 1. Explain how the graph shows this. *(1 mark)*

17 The graph shows the volume of carbon dioxide produced when excess limestone is added to $100\,cm^3$ of hydrochloric acid at room temperature.

a) Use the graph to find:

  i) the volume of carbon dioxide produced after 20 seconds *(1 mark)*

  ii) the time taken for the reaction to stop. *(1 mark)*

b) On the graph, draw the curve you would expect if the reaction were repeated using exactly the same volume and concentration of acid at a higher temperature, with the limestone still in excess. *(2 marks)*

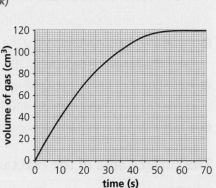

Go online for answers

Online

Rate of chemical change 2

Explaining the rate of a reaction

A chemical reaction occurs when the reacting particles collide with one another. Not all collisions result in a chemical reaction: the collision needs enough energy for bonds in the reactant molecules to break.

In the diagram, particles of two different reacting gases are shown in yellow and red. All the particles are moving at high speed in random directions. When one of the red particles collides with one of the yellow particles with enough energy, then a reaction will occur.

The number of **successful** collisions is a small percentage of the total number of collisions taking place in a given time. The number of successful collisions per second is called the **collision frequency**. The higher the collision frequency, the higher the rate of reaction.

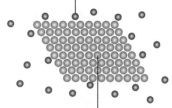

⬆ **When particles of reacting gases collide with sufficient energy a chemical reaction will occur**

Factors affecting the rate of chemical change

The temperature of the reactants

A higher temperature means a higher rate of reaction. This is because:

● increasing the temperature of the reactants increases the mean velocity of the particles

● faster particles means that more of the collisions will have enough energy for a reaction to take place – the **collision frequency** increases

● a higher collision frequency means a higher rate of reaction.

The concentration of the reactants

A higher concentration means a higher rate of reaction. This is because:

● increasing the concentration of the reactants increases the total number of reacting particles in the same volume

● more particles per unit volume means there are likely to be more collisions with enough energy and so the collision frequency increases

● a higher collision frequency means a higher rate of reaction.

The surface area of the reactants

A higher surface area means a higher rate of reaction. This is because:

● increasing the surface area allows more of the reactants to collide with each other with enough energy

● more collisions causes a higher collision frequency and so a higher rate of reaction.

red particles can hit the outer layer of green particles

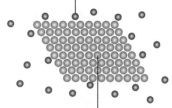

... but not those in the centre of the lump

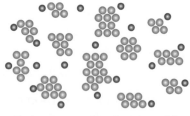

with the same number of green particles now split into lots of smaller bits, there are hardly any green particles that the red particles can't get at

⬆ **Powders react at a faster rate than lumps**

Using a catalyst

Revised

A **catalyst** can also increase the rate of reaction.

- Catalysts are substances that increase the rate of a chemical reaction but remain chemically unchanged at the end of the reaction.

- Many catalysts work only for one particular reaction.

- Some industrial reactions are only possible on large scales by using a catalyst.

- A catalyst works because it provides a 'surface' on which the reacting molecules can collide with each other – this reduces the amount of energy needed for a collision to be successful.

- More particles will have the minimum amount of energy required, increasing the collision frequency and the rate of reaction.

The importance of catalysts

Revised

Catalysts are used in the production of bulk chemicals, fine chemicals, petrochemicals and in food processing: 90% of all commercial chemical products involve catalysts at some stage in the manufacture.

The use of catalysts in chemical processes has huge importance, not only in economic terms. Catalysts reduce the amount of energy required to produce chemical products. This in turn preserves world fuel reserves and reduces the environmental impact of burning fossil fuels, e.g. global warming.

> **Examiner tip**
>
> When you have to plot a graph in an exam, you usually have to devise a suitable scale for each axis, plot the points correctly and draw a suitable line of best-fit. Make sure that your axes have linear scales. Check that you have plotted all the points correctly. Remember that best-fit lines can be curves as well as straight lines.

Check your understanding

Tested

18 a) Fillers can be used to fill dents in car bodies. These work by mixing a paste with a small quantity of hardener. The paste does not harden until the hardener is added. The hardener acts as a catalyst for the reaction. State what is meant by a catalyst. *(2 marks)*

b) A student wanted to find out if the amount of catalyst made a difference to the rate at which the paste hardened. She mixed a fixed amount of paste with different volumes of catalyst and recorded the time it took for the paste to harden at room temperature, 20 °C. The results obtained are given in the table.

Volume of hardener added to paste (cm³)	Time taken for paste to harden (min)
0.5	15.0
1.0	7.5
1.5	5.0
2.0	3.5
2.5	2.0
3.0	2.0

   i) On a piece of graph paper, draw a graph of the results. *(4 marks)*

   ii) Using your graph, describe what the results tell you. *(2 marks)*

   iii) State what you would expect to happen to the reaction rate if the experiments were repeated at 50 °C. *(1 mark)*

Go online for answers

Online

Fractional distillation

The crude oil that is extracted from oil wells is a complex mixture of **hydrocarbons** – compounds that contain only carbon and hydrogen. Crude oil can be separated into less complex mixtures, known as fractions, by the process of **fractional distillation**.

The process

Revised

The hydrocarbons in the crude oil have different boiling points. This property is used to separate them. The longer the carbon chain in the molecule of the chemical, the higher the boiling point.

- The crude oil is heated as it enters a fractional distillation column, or **fractionating column**.

- When the temperature approaches the boiling point of some of the hydrocarbons, these will **evaporate** from the oil.

- The vapour will rise in the column, away from the heat, and will cool as it rises.

- When the vapour cools below its boiling point, it will **condense**.

- The hydrocarbons with bigger molecules have higher boiling points. These will not rise so far in the column before the vapour condenses.

- At the point where they condense, the hydrocarbons can be collected. Each **fraction** has a different collecting point.

- The fractions are treated after collection to remove impurities.

> **Examiner tip**
>
> You will not be expected to remember the names of the fractions or their boiling points, just the general principles that the higher you go in the column, the molecules collected are smaller and have lower boiling points.

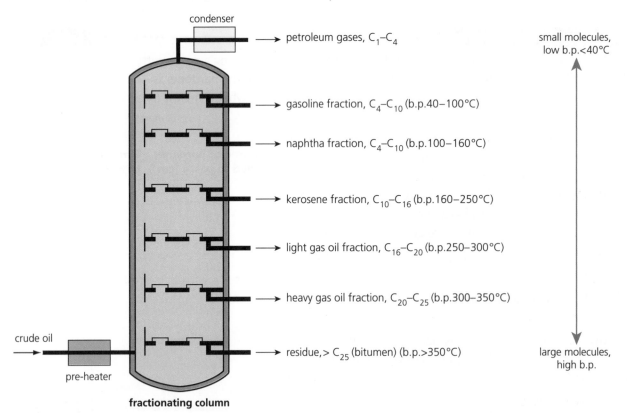

↑ **Fractional distillation of crude oil**

The importance of boiling points

Revised

Some hydrocarbons have such low boiling points that they do not condense. These are collected as a gas at the top of the column.

Others have such high boiling points that they do not evaporate. These are 'left over' as residue and collected from the bottom of the column.

A number of hydrocarbons have similar boiling points. The process cannot separate each one, so the fractions collected are still mixtures.

Check your understanding

Tested

19 The diagram shows a fractional distillation column.

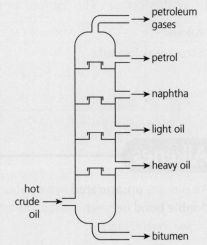

   a) The naphtha fraction is collected from a higher point in the fractionating column than the light oil fraction. Explain what this tells you about:

   i) the size of the molecules in the two fractions. *(1 mark)*

   ii) the boiling points of the two fractions. *(1 mark)*

   b) State why bitumen has to be run off from the bottom of the column. *(1 mark)*

   c) The fractions are all mixtures of **hydrocarbons**. What is a hydrocarbon? *(1 mark)*

20 The graph below shows the demand for different fractions of crude oil, and the amounts produced.

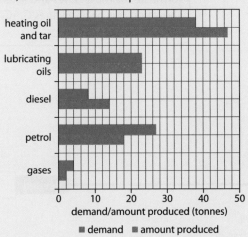

   a) What is the demand for diesel? *(1 mark)*

   b) For which fraction does demand exactly match the amount produced? *(1 mark)*

   c) By how much does the demand for petrol exceed the amount produced? *(1 mark)*

   d) Explain how crude oil is separated into different fractions. *(6 marks QWC)*

Go online for answers

Online

Alkanes and alkenes

Alkanes and **alkenes** are different types of **hydrocarbon**.

> **Examiner tip**
> Remember that a hydrocarbon is a compound that contains only the elements carbon and hydrogen.

Alkanes

Revised

Alkanes are **saturated** hydrocarbons. Their molecules contain **single bonds** only, which means they are 'saturated' with hydrogen (i.e. they contain as much hydrogen as possible).

There are different alkanes, the difference being the number of carbon atoms they contain. The first four are shown in the table.

Alkane	Methane CH_4	Ethane C_2H_6	Propane C_3H_8	Butane C_4H_{10}
Structural formula	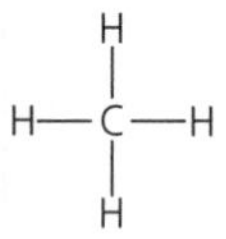	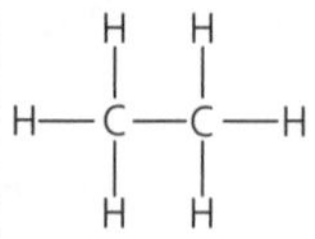	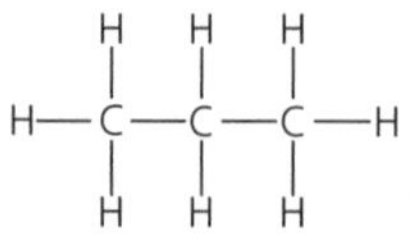	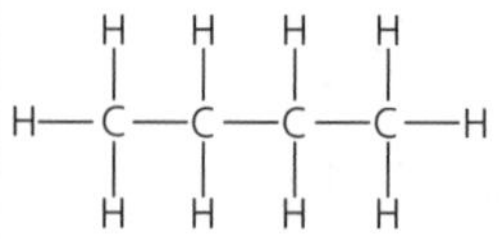

Alkenes

Revised

Alkenes are **unsaturated** hydrocarbons. Their molecules have at least one **double bond** between carbon atoms. The structures of two alkenes are shown in the diagram.

Alkene	Ethene C_2H_4	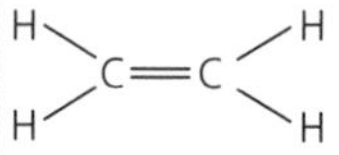
Structural formula	Propene C_3H_6	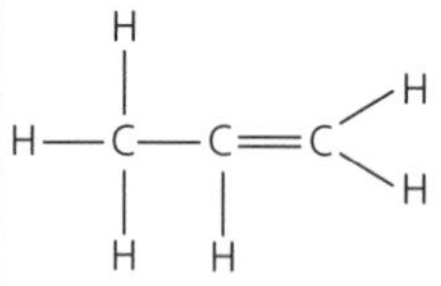

> **Examiner tip**
> You need to be able to both **recognise** and **draw** the structural formulae for the alkanes and alkenes shown on this page: alkanes C_1–C_4 and alkenes C_2–C_3.

Addition reactions

Revised

The presence of at least one carbon–carbon double bond in alkenes means that other atoms can be added to the molecule. Reactions that do this are called **addition reactions**. Hydrogen and bromine can be added in this way.

When hydrogen is added to an alkene (**hydrogenation**), the corresponding alkane is formed. This reaction is carried out by heating the alkene under pressure, in the presence of a metallic catalyst. The hydrogenation of ethene to form ethane is shown below.

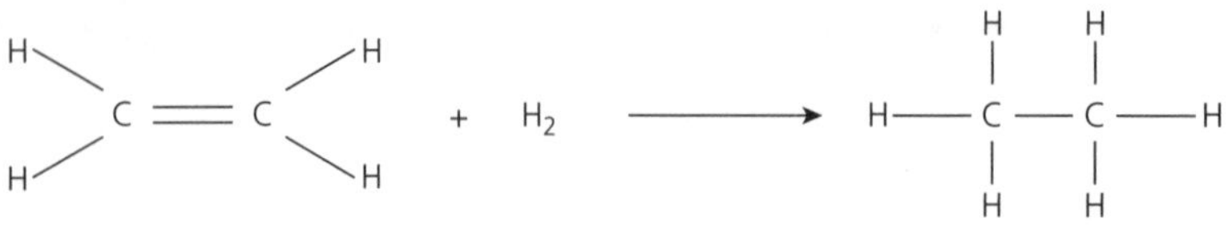

ethene hydrogen ethane

↑ **Hydrogenation of ethene**

When bromine is added to an alkene it forms a **dibromoalkane**. The double bond breaks and two bromine atoms attach. This reaction is useful because it can be used to test for the presence of an alkene. Brown/orange bromine water reacts with the alkene and its colour disappears because the product formed is colourless. The reaction is shown in the diagram.

$$Br_2 + C_2H_4 \longrightarrow BrCH_2CH_2Br$$

bromine   ethene   dibromoethane

↑ **Addition reaction of ethene with bromine. There is one bromine atom on each carbon atom in the product formed**

Check your understanding

Tested

21 a) The structural formulae of some hydrocarbons are shown below. One structural formula is missing.

methane   ethane   propane   butane   pentane

   i)   Name the **two** elements present in all hydrocarbons. (1 mark)

   ii) Give the name of the hydrocarbon in the figure above which is represented by the molecular formula C_2H_6. (1 mark)

   iii) Butane contains four carbon atoms and ten hydrogen atoms. Draw the structural formula for butane. (1 mark)

   b) **Name** the alkene which has the structural formula shown here: (1 mark)

22 a) The structural formulae of four hydrocarbons are shown below. **Use only this information** to answer parts (i), (ii) and (iii).

   A   B   C   D

   i)   Give the molecular formula for hydrocarbon C. (1 mark)

   ii) Give the letter of an **unsaturated** hydrocarbon. (1 mark)

   iii) Explain your choice of letter in part (ii). (1 mark)

   b) What name is given to the group of hydrocarbons that includes hydrocarbon A? (1 mark)

   c) What name is given to the group of hydrocarbons that includes hydrocarbons B–D? (1 mark)

   d) i) How could hydrocarbon A be converted into hydrocarbon B? (1 mark)

   ii) What name is given to this type of reaction? (1 mark)

Go online for answers

Online

Polymerisation and plastics

Polymers

Revised

A **polymer** is a compound which has large molecules, with a high relative molecular mass. It is formed from long chains of smaller molecules, which are called **monomers**.

Polymers come in two types:

● **addition polymers**, which are made from only one monomer

● **condensation polymers**, which are made from two or more different monomers.

Polymerisation of alkenes

Revised

Alkene molecules can be assembled together in large numbers to make a variety of useful polymers, such as polythene, polypropene, polytetrafluoroethene (PTFE) and polyvinylchloride (PVC).

Ethene molecules can be **polymerised** to form the addition polymer poly(ethene), more commonly known as **polythene**. This is done by heating ethene under pressure. The number of molecules that join up varies, but is generally between 2000 and 20 000. The polymerisation of ethene is shown here.

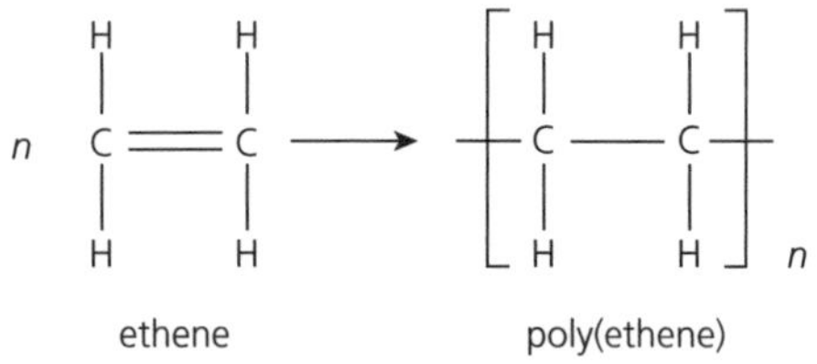

> **Examiner tip**
>
> The symbol **n** in the diagram is used to mean 'a large number'. The polymer molecule is too large to draw its whole structural formula, so it is given in the form of a **repeating unit** (the part inside the brackets). It is important that you include the **n** in any exam answer.

$$n \; C = C \longrightarrow \left[C - C \right]_n$$

ethene   poly(ethene)

⬆ **Polymerisation of ethene**

Note that since only ethene is involved in the polymerisation, this is an **addition polymerisation**.

Polymerisation of alkenes involves the breaking of the carbon–carbon double bond, with each carbon then attaching to a carbon of another ethene molecule.

Different polymers

Revised

Polymers of different alkenes form a variety of plastics. The ones you need to know are shown below.

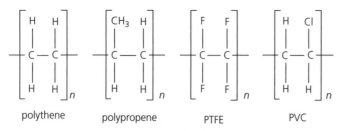

polythene   polypropene   PTFE   PVC

⬆ **Repeating units of some important polymers**

Thermoplastics and thermosets

Plastics can be divided into two types, depending on their reaction to heating.

- Plastics that soften when heated are called **thermoplastics**.

- Plastics that are resistant to heat are called **thermosets**.

- Thermoplastics are made up of polymer chains that are not linked together and so they can slide over one another, resulting in them being easy to melt. Examples are polythene, PVC and polypropene.

- Thermosets have polymer chains with strong **cross linkages** which hold the structure together and make them resistant to heat. They can be moulded, by setting the liquid thermoset with **heat**, **chemical reactions** or **radiation**. Once set, they cannot be re-melted. Examples are Bakelite and epoxy resin.

Check your understanding

23 The table below shows some information about monomers and the polymers that can be made from them.

Name of monomer	Structural formula of monomer	Name of polymer	Repeating unit of polymer
	$\begin{array}{c} H \quad\quad H \\ C=C \\ H \quad\quad H \end{array}$	Poly(ethene) or polythene	$\left[\begin{array}{cc} H & H \\ -C-C- \\ H & H \end{array}\right]_n$
Tetrafluoroethene	$\begin{array}{c} F \quad\quad F \\ C=C \\ F \quad\quad F \end{array}$	Polytetrafluoroethene (PTFE)	
Vinylchloride		Polyvinylchloride (PVC)	$\left[\begin{array}{cc} H & Cl \\ -C-C- \\ H & H \end{array}\right]_n$

a) Write the name/draw the structures to complete the table. *(3 marks)*

b) All three polymers in the table are formed by the same type of polymerisation. Give the **name** for this type of polymerisation. *(1 mark)*

24 The pictures show a plastic plug, and the arrangement of polymer chains in the plastic.

a) What name is given to the type of plastic used in the plug? *(1 mark)*

b) The plastic is very rigid (cannot be bent or stretched). Explain why it has this property. *(2 marks)*

c) Suggest why this type of plastic is used for making electrical plugs. *(2 marks)*

↑ Electrical plug

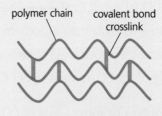

polymer chain   covalent bond crosslink

↑ Arrangement of polymer chains

Go online for answers

Chemical calculations 1

Percentage composition of simple compounds

Revised ☐

Relative atomic masses, A_r, (from a Periodic Table) allow us to work out the **relative molecular mass** (or **relative formula mass**), M_r, of a compound.

The **percentage composition** (by mass) of the elements in a compound can then be calculated.

Example

1 Find the percentage composition (by mass) of carbon and oxygen in carbon dioxide.

In the carbon dioxide (CO_2) molecule there is one carbon atom and two oxygen atoms, so the relative molecular mass is:
$M_r = [12 + (2 \times 16)] = 44$.

$$\text{Percentage of C in } CO_2 = \frac{\text{total relative mass of C in } CO_2}{\text{relative molecular mass of } CO_2} \times 100\%$$

$$= \frac{12}{44} \times 100\% = 27.3\%$$

$$\text{Percentage of O in } CO_2 = \frac{\text{total relative mass of O in } CO_2}{\text{relative molecular mass of } CO_2} \times 100\%$$

$$= \frac{32}{44} \times 100\% = 72.7\%$$

> **Examiner tip**
>
> You need to work carefully and methodically when doing chemical calculation questions. If you are given a table of data, make sure you copy the numbers correctly. Make sure you use a calculator to check your numerical answers, and aim to check numerical calculations several times.

Masses of reactants and products

Revised ☐

Relative molecular (or formula) masses and a balanced symbol equation can be used to predict the relationships between the masses of reacting substances and the products they form.

Example

2 Find the mass of carbon dioxide formed when 5.3 g of sodium carbonate completely reacts with excess hydrochloric acid.

The balanced symbol equation is:

$Na_2CO_3(s) + 2HCl(aq) \longrightarrow 2NaCl(aq) + H_2O(l) + CO_2(g)$

Relative formula mass of sodium carbonate = 106

Relative molecular mass of carbon dioxide = 44

106 g of Na_2CO_3 forms 44 g of CO_2

1 g of Na_2CO_3 forms $\dfrac{44}{106}$ g of CO_2

5.3 g of Na_2CO_3 forms $\dfrac{44}{106} \times 5.3$ g of CO_2

So mass of carbon dioxide formed = 2.2 g

Yield of a chemical reaction

The meaning of the terms **theoretical yield** and **actual yield** are shown in the following example.

Example

3 The reaction of magnesium with oxygen produces magnesium oxide, MgO. The balanced equation is:

$$2Mg(s) + O_2(g) \longrightarrow 2MgO(s)$$

Find the theoretical yield of magnesium oxide if 5 g of magnesium is used.

Relative atomic mass of magnesium = 24

Relative atomic mass of oxygen = 16

So relative formula mass of magnesium oxide = 40

The equation tells us that:

$(2 \times 24) = 48$ g magnesium gives $(2 \times 40) = 80$ g magnesium oxide

1 g magnesium makes $\dfrac{80}{48} = 1.67$ g magnesium oxide

Using 5 g of magnesium you would expect to get $(5 \times 1.67) = 8.35$ g of magnesium oxide. This is the **theoretical yield** of the reaction.

If only 7.9 g of magnesium oxide is produced, this is called the **actual yield** of the reaction.

The **percentage yield** of a reaction is calculated by:

$$\text{percentage yield} = \frac{\text{actual yield}}{\text{theoretical yield}} \times 100\%$$

Check your understanding

25 **a)** When chlorine gas is passed over heated iron filings, a brown solid is formed. During an experiment the following results were obtained:

Mass of iron filings and container = 3.660 g

Mass of iron chloride formed and the container = 4.725 g

Mass of container = 3.100 g

Calculate:

i) the mass of the iron filings used   *(1 mark)*

ii) the mass of the chlorine used   *(1 mark)*

iii) the simplest formula of the iron chloride.   *(2 marks)*

[A_r(Fe) = 56, A_r(Cl) = 35.5] Working must be shown in your answers.

b) Magnesium reacts with oxygen to form magnesium oxide. The balanced symbol equation for the reaction is shown below.

$$2Mg + O_2 \longrightarrow 2MgO$$

i) Use the equation for the reaction between magnesium and oxygen to calculate the maximum mass of magnesium oxide formed when 12 g of magnesium reacts with excess of oxygen.   *(3 marks)*

ii) During an actual experiment, only 18 g of magnesium oxide was formed from 12 g of magnesium. Calculate the percentage yield of the reaction.

(2 marks)

Go online for answers

Chemical calculations 2

Calculating energy changes

When chemical reactions occur, new substances (the products) are formed from the reacting substances (the reactants). Reactions involve breaking bonds in the reactants and reforming bonds to form the products.

● Breaking bonds is endothermic – it requires energy to be put in.

● Formation of bonds is exothermic – it gives out energy.

The energy values for selected covalent bonds are shown in the table.

The difference between the total energy needed to break all the bonds and the total energy given out when the new bonds are formed determines whether the overall reaction is **exothermic** (gives out heat) or **endothermic** (takes in heat).

Bond	Bond energy (kJ)
O=O	496
C–H	412
H–H	436
C=O	743
O–H	463
C–C	348
N≡N	944
C=C	612
N–H	388

↑ **Energy values for covalent bonds**

Example

Consider the complete combustion of methane given by the formulae:

methane + oxygen $\longrightarrow$ carbon dioxide + water

$CH_4(g) + 2O_2(g) \longrightarrow CO_2(g) + 2H_2O(g)$

The bonds broken and formed during the reaction are shown below:

| shows the breaking of a bond   ▼ shows the formation of a bond

The bonds broken are four C–H bonds and two O=O bonds, so the total energy put in is:

$4 \times$ C–H $= (4 \times 412) = 1648\,kJ$

$2 \times$ O=O $= (2 \times 496) = 992\,kJ$

total energy in = 2640 kJ

The bonds formed are two C=O bonds and four O–H bonds:

$2 \times$ C=O $= (2 \times 743) = 1486\,kJ$

$4 \times$ O–H $= (4 \times 463) = 1852\,kJ$

total energy out = 3338 kJ

The overall energy change is:

total energy needed to break all bonds – total energy given out when new bonds are formed

$= 2640 - 3338 = -698\,kJ$

In this case, the amount of energy given out to the surroundings is more than the amount taken in so the reaction is exothermic.

Exothermic reactions **give out heat** to the surroundings.

Endothermic reactions **take in heat** from the surroundings.

Examiner tip

Chemical calculation questions require you to work carefully and methodically. **Make sure you use a calculator** to check your numerical answers. If you are given a table of data, (or you take data off the Periodic Table at the back of your examination paper), make sure you copy the numbers correctly. **Always check numerical calculations several times after you have done them.**

26 When chlorine reacts with hydrogen, hydrogen chloride is formed.

$$H—H + Cl—Cl \longrightarrow \begin{array}{c} H—Cl \\ H—Cl \end{array}$$

The relative amounts of energy needed to break individual bonds are shown in the table.

Bond	Amount of energy needed to break bond (kJ)
H–H	436
Cl–Cl	243
H–Cl	432

a) Use the bond energy values in the table to calculate the relative energy:

  i) needed to break all the bonds in the reactants   *(2 marks)*

  ii) released when the bonds in the product are formed.   *(2 marks)*

b) Using your answers to parts **(a)(i)** and **(ii)**, explain why the relative overall energy change for the reaction is exothermic.   *(1 mark)*

27 Hydrogen peroxide, H_2O_2, decomposes very slowly to produce water and oxygen gas. The reaction taking place is shown by the following equation.

$$2H_2O_2 \longrightarrow 2H_2O + O_2$$

$$\begin{array}{c} H—O—O—H \\ \\ H—O—O—H \end{array} \longrightarrow \begin{array}{c} H\!\diagdown\!\diagup\!H \\ O \end{array} \; + \; O\!=\!O$$

$$\begin{array}{c} H\!\diagdown\!\diagup\!H \\ O \end{array}$$

The relative amounts of energy needed to break individual bonds are shown in the table below.

Note: the amount of energy released in making a bond is equal and opposite to that needed to break the bond.

Bond	Amount of energy needed to break bond (kJ)
H–O	464
O=O	498
O–O	144

Use the bond energy values in the table to show that the overall energy change for the reaction is −210 kJ.   *(5 marks)*

28 When hydrogen burns in air water is formed. The overall relative energy change during the reaction is −486 kJ, showing that the reaction is exothermic.

a) The total energy needed to break all the bonds in the reactants is 1370 kJ. Calculate the total energy released when the bonds in the product are formed.   *(1 mark)*

b) Calculate the amount of energy released in forming an O–H bond.   *(2 marks)*

Go online for answers ⎯ Online

Water supply and conservation

Water treatment

Water supplied to homes and businesses for drinking has to meet high standards for safety. Visible impurities have to be removed, but so do bacteria which could be harmful to health.

Our drinking water comes from rivers, lakes or underground sources, and is stored in reservoirs before being treated. The process of water treatment is shown in the diagram below.

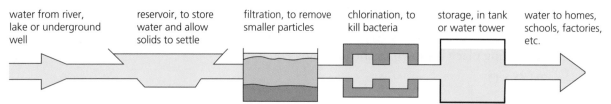

water from river, lake or underground well

reservoir, to store water and allow solids to settle

filtration, to remove smaller particles

chlorination, to kill bacteria

storage, in tank or water tower

water to homes, schools, factories, etc.

↑ **Stages in the treatment of drinking water**

There are three stages to the process:

● **Sedimentation**. Water is first stored in settling tanks, where larger particles sink to the bottom. Water can be drawn off, leaving the sediment behind.

● **Filtration**. The water is then passed through a system of filters, which remove small particles. Bacteria, however, can pass through the filters.

● **Chlorination**. Chlorine is added to the water, which kill the bacteria, leaving the water fit for delivery.

The importance of conserving water

Although there is a very large amount of water on the planet, much of it is inaccessible or unsuitable for use. The amount of water available via rainfall varies from place to place and from season to season. If the demand for water exceeds the supply, severe consequences could result, because water is very important for humans and their environment.

● We need a supply of drinking water. Humans can only live for about a week without any water.

● Water is needed on farms to grow food.

● The amount of water is important in any habitat. If it is reduced, the habitat will change and certain species may be unable to survive.

● Water is important in many industrial processes, especially for cooling machinery.

● Washing things (including ourselves) with water is important for hygiene.

> **Examiner tip**
> When revising, you do not need to learn all the reasons and methods for conserving water. Questions will ask for examples, so try to remember three or four for each.

Ways of conserving water

In order to ensure a sustainable supply of water, homes and businesses need to avoid using water unnecessarily. There are many ways this can be done:

- having a shower rather than a bath
- not using too much water to flush the toilet
- not letting water run unnecessarily (e.g. when cleaning your teeth)
- repairing dripping taps
- collecting rainwater to use for watering the garden or washing a car
- watering houseplants with waste water from washing up
- only using a washing machine or a dishwasher when it is full
- water companies fixing leaking supply pipes
- businesses promoting water conservation at work
- installing irrigation systems on farms that use less water.

> **Examiner tip**
>
> Note that some questions, such as Question **29** below, may seem to ask for information that you have not learnt (such as the use of sand in filter beds). The required information is probably, as here, given in the question. Always read the question through carefully.

Check your understanding

Tested

29 Read the information below.

Most tap water in Wales comes from rivers, lakes and reservoirs. The flow diagram shows the stages in water purification.

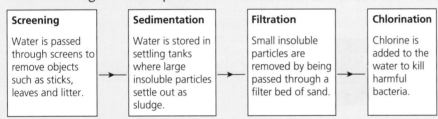

Screening	Sedimentation	Filtration	Chlorination
Water is passed through screens to remove objects such as sticks, leaves and litter.	Water is stored in settling tanks where large insoluble particles settle out as sludge.	Small insoluble particles are removed by being passed through a filter bed of sand.	Chlorine is added to the water to kill harmful bacteria.

Use **only the information above** to answer parts **(a)–(d)**.

a) Name **two** sources of tap water. *(1 mark)*

b) Give the name of the stage which removes

   i) litter *(1 mark)*

   ii) large insoluble particles. *(1 mark)*

c) Name the material used in filter beds. *(1 mark)*

d) Give the reason for adding chlorine to water. *(1 mark)*

30 The graph below shows the annual rainfall in the UK between 2000 and 2011.

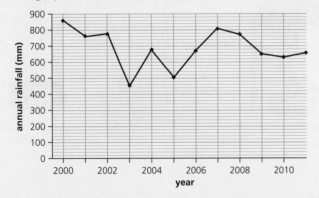

a) What is the overall trend in rainfall in the UK between 2000 and 2011? *(1 mark)*

b) Why were hosepipe bans introduced in 2007 but not in 2011? *(1 mark)*

c) List **three** ways in which householders can conserve water. *(3 marks)*

Go online for answers

Online

Purification of water and solubility

Desalination of water

There is a huge amount of water in the sea, but people cannot drink sea water. There is technology that can **desalinate** sea water (remove the salt from it), but there are problems associated with doing this on a large scale across the world.

- The process uses much more energy than other processes used to produce drinking water.
- This makes the process **expensive**. Many countries that have the most need for water are poor and cannot afford desalination.
- The desalination produces **greenhouse gases**, whereas normal water treatment plants produce very little.
- The very salty water left when the fresh water has been extracted is a **pollutant**.
- Countries with no coastline would have to pump sea water across large distances.

Separating water from other miscible liquids

Some liquids (e.g. ethanol) are **miscible** with water, that is, they mix with the water and so cannot be easily separated from it. It is possible however to separate such mixtures by the process of distillation.

Distillation uses the fact that the liquid mixed with the water will have a different boiling point. The mixture is heated, and when the temperature approaches the boiling point of one of the liquids in the mixture, that liquid will evaporate and can be collected by condensation. At 100 °C, the liquid collected will be pure water. In the laboratory, the apparatus used to carry out this procedure is called a condenser (see diagram).

The thermometer is used to take the temperature of the vapour (so that it can be identified). The cold water entering the condenser cools the vapour so that it condenses. The liquid that condenses is called the distillate.

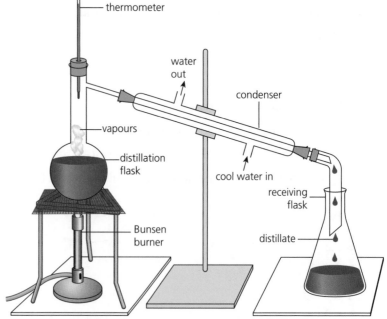

thermometer

water out

condenser

vapours

distillation flask

cool water in

receiving flask

Bunsen burner

distillate

↑ **Distillation in the laboratory**

Solubility curves

Revised

Different amounts of a substance can dissolve in a solvent, e.g. water, at different temperatures. This effect is shown by a graph called a **solubility curve**. A solution that can still dissolve more solute is **unsaturated**. A solution that cannot dissolve any more solute is **saturated**.

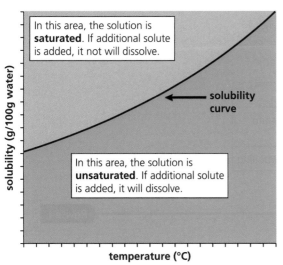

In this area, the solution is **saturated**. If additional solute is added, it not will dissolve.

solubility curve

In this area, the solution is **unsaturated**. If additional solute is added, it will dissolve.

↑ A solubility curve

Examiner tip

You will not be expected to remember the shape of any particular solubility curve. You will always be given the data, and asked to interpret it.

Check your understanding

Tested

31 The graph opposite shows the solubility of potassium nitrate and four substances, A, B, C and D, in water at various temperatures.

Use the graph to answer parts **(a)–(e)**.

Give the letter of the substance which:

a) has the **lowest** solubility at 70 °C   (1 mark)

b) has the same solubility as potassium nitrate at 53 °C   (1 mark)

c) has the solubility that changes the least with temperature   (1 mark)

d) forms 21 g of solid when a saturated solution in 100 g of water at 65 °C is cooled to 40 °C   (1 mark)

e) forms the smallest mass of solid when a saturated solution in 100 g of water at 20 °C is cooled to 0 °C.   (1 mark)

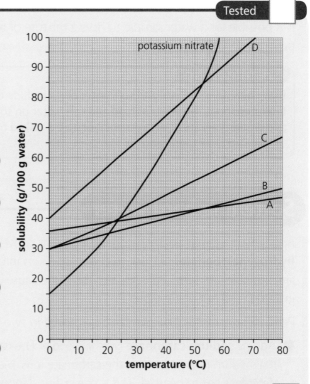

Go online for answers

Online

Hard and soft water

What we mean by hard water
Revised

Water is termed either 'hard' or 'soft' according to which substances are dissolved in it.

Hard water contains dissolved **calcium** (Ca^{2+}) and **magnesium** (Mg^{2+}) **ions**. The hardness may be **temporary** or **permanent**. The differences between temporary and permanent hard water are shown in the table.

Temporary hard water	Permanent hard water
Contains calcium and/or magnesium hydrogencarbonates	Contains calcium and/or magnesium sulfates and/or chlorides
Hardness can be removed by boiling	Hardness cannot be removed by boiling

Testing for hardness
Revised

You can tell the difference between hard and soft water by seeing how well the water lathers when soap is added and the water is shaken. It is difficult to produce a lather in hard water, whereas soft water lathers easily.

If a water sample can produce more lather only after it has been boiled, it must be temporary hard water. If boiling has no effect, it is permanent hard water.

It is possible for a water sample to have a mixture of temporary and permanent hardness.

Examiner tip

Exam questions on hard and soft water often include data for you to interpret about the effect of hard and soft water on soap. You may be asked questions about experimental design, or asked to draw conclusions or evaluate the experiment.

Softening hard water
Revised

Boiling removes temporary hardness because it converts the **hydrogencarbonates** of calcium and magnesium into **carbonates**, which are insoluble and form a precipitate. This is the cause of limescale or 'fur' in kettles and hot water pipes

Permanent hardness of water can be removed in two ways.

- Adding **sodium carbonate** (washing soda). The calcium and magnesium ions bond with the carbonate ions, meaning that less detergent has to be used. This is cheap, but deposits still form.
- Passing the water through an **ion exchange column**. This removes the calcium and magnesium ions and replaces them with **sodium ions**, which do not cause hardness. This is effective but expensive.

Advantages and disadvantages of hard water

Revised

Advantages

● Many people think that hard water tastes better than soft water.

● Calcium and magnesium are essential minerals in the diet, and hard water can provide them.

● The magnesium in hard water may give some protection against heart disease.

Disadvantages

● Temporary hard water can produce deposits which clog and damage hot water pipes, boilers and kettle elements.

● Hard water requires more soap or detergent to clean effectively.

● Treating permanent hard water in order to save on detergent can produce deposits on washed clothes.

Check your understanding

Tested

32 a) 1 cm³ of soap solution was shaken, the same number of times, with 20 cm³ of four different metal chloride solutions with equal concentrations of the chloride ions. The results are shown in the diagram below.

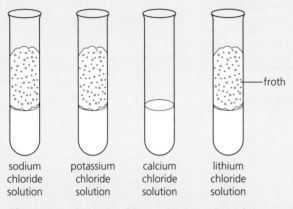

| sodium chloride solution | potassium chloride solution | calcium chloride solution | lithium chloride solution |

froth

  i) Name the **metal ion** which makes the water hard. *(1 mark)*

  ii) How do the observations tell you that it is not the chloride ions that make the water hard? *(1 mark)*

b) Boiling hard water forms scale on elements in electric kettles. The presence of the limescale results in energy being wasted. The graph shows the effect of limescale on the percentage of energy wasted.

  i) State how the percentage of energy wasted depends on the thickness of limescale. *(1 mark)*

  ii) Use the graph to give the percentage of energy wasted if no limescale were present. *(1 mark)*

c) Give **one** reason why living in a hard water area can be beneficial to your health. *(1 mark)*

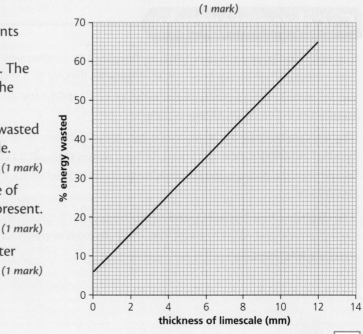

Chromatography and spectroscopy

Chromatography is a technique for separating the components of a mixture. The technique exists in several forms.

Paper chromatography

Revised

A spot of a chemical mixture, such as ink, which contains a number of pigments, is placed on some absorbent **chromatography paper**. The paper is placed in a solvent. As the solvent soaks into the paper, it dissolves the pigments in the ink and moves them up the paper. The very soluble pigments will travel with the solvent, whereas less soluble pigments will get left behind. Gradually the different pigments become spread out on the paper.

The distance that a substance travels up the paper allows scientists to identify which substance it is. They do this by calculating its **R_f value**. The method for doing this is shown in the diagram.

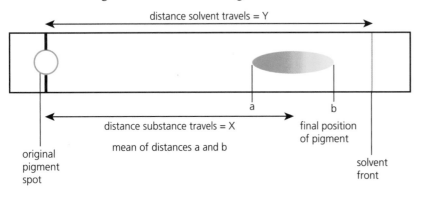

$$R_f \text{ value} = \frac{\text{distance substance travels (X)}}{\text{distance solvent travels (Y)}}$$

⬆ **Calculation of R_f value**

Gas chromatography

Revised

Gas chromatography is an analytical technique used by chemists to detect and measure small amounts of certain chemicals present in a mixture. It can be used to detect pollutants in water or in air, and to test for banned substances in the blood of sports players.

The mixture must be in the form of a gas, either naturally, or by the heating and vaporisation of a liquid. The gas passes through a column and the different substances are absorbed onto an inert solid or liquid inside the column.

The distance the substances travel along the column is determined by their chemical and physical properties. Their position in the column is detected electronically.

Atomic spectroscopy

Another technique used by professional analytical chemists to find out which atoms or ions are present in a sample is **atomic spectroscopy**. It can identify the substances and their concentrations in many different types of sample, for example biological tissues.

The technique uses the interaction of **electromagnetic radiation** (such as X-rays, ultra-violet and visible light) with atoms in a device called a **spectrometer**. This may be one of various types:

- atomic absorption spectrometer
- optical spectrometer
- X-ray fluorescence spectrometer.

All types can detect and measure very small quantities of atoms or ions.

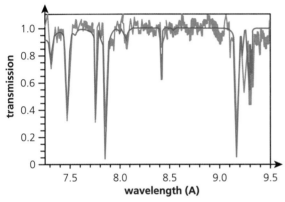

↑ Each peak on the spectrum shows the presence of one type of atom or ion

Examiner tip

Gas chromatography and atomic spectroscopy are new in the WJEC specification from 2012, so you won't see questions on them in past papers. You need to know what they are and how they are used, rather than details about the techniques. You will also need to be able to interpret data from the techniques.

Check your understanding

Tested

33 The diagram alongside shows the apparatus used to investigate the different dyes in five felt-tipped pens, A, B, C, D and E.

The following chromatograms were obtained from the five different coloured pens.

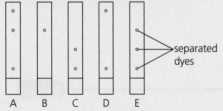

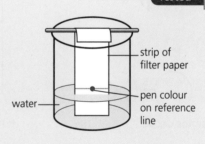

a) Give the letter of the pen which contains:

   i) both the dyes found also in pen D *(1 mark)*

   ii) the dyes found also in both pens B and C. *(1 mark)*

b) Pencils made from graphite are usually used to draw the reference line on the strips of filter paper used in chromatography experiments. Give the property of graphite that makes a pencil a more suitable choice than ink for drawing the reference lines. *(1 mark)*

c) Describe how you would find the **original** colour of pen A from its chromatogram. *(1 mark)*

Go online for answers

Online

Simple electrical circuits 1

Current

The current flowing through electrical components in a circuit is measured in amperes (or amps), A, using an ammeter connected in series with the components.

Series circuits

For components connected **in series**, the current is the same at any point in the circuit. This means that all the components in a series circuit have the same current flowing through them. In the diagram below the ammeter at A will read the same as an ammeter connected into the circuit at B or C.

Parallel circuits

When components are connected **in parallel**, the current splits when it gets to a junction in the circuit. No current is lost at a junction so the total current into the junction equals the total current out of the junction. In the diagram, the current at P is equal to the current at Q **plus** the current at R; the current at X **plus** the current at Y is equal to the current at Z.

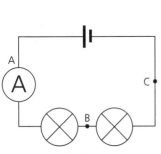

↑ **A series circuit**

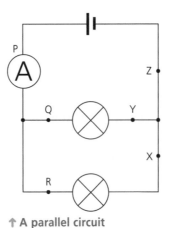

↑ **A parallel circuit**

> ### Examiner tip
> Questions involving circuit diagrams require you to 'read' the diagram before attempting the question. Identify all the components, decide if the components are arranged in series or parallel and pay particular attention to any labels next to components – they will have been put there for a reason.

Voltage

The voltage across components in a circuit is measured in volts using a voltmeter. Voltmeters are always connected in parallel across components.

In parallel circuits like the second circuit diagram above, the voltage is the same across each of the bulbs. A voltmeter connected between Q and Y will read the same voltage as one connected between R and X.

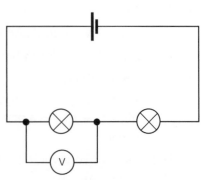

↑ **The voltmeter measures the voltage across one bulb**

Electrical circuits in the home

Most of the mains electrical circuits in your house are connected in parallel. This has several advantages:

● If one component in the circuit stops working, all the others will continue to work properly.

● The voltage is the same for all the components.

● It is much easier to connect up all the circuits, and to add new circuits.

● It is easy to work out the total current being drawn by the different parts of the circuit (it all adds up).

● It is safer – each part of the circuit can be protected by its own fuse or circuit breaker and controlled by its own switch.

Check your understanding

1   The diagram shows part of a mains lighting circuit protected by a fuse in the household fuse box (consumer unit). A, B and C are lamps; S_1, S_2 and S_3 are switches.

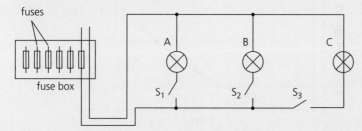

a) Underline **two** words which correctly complete the sentence below.   *(2 marks)*

If too much current is drawn by the lighting circuit, the fuse will melt, this makes the circuit (**complete/incomplete**) and the lamps will be (**on/off**).

b) The fuse in this circuit is working properly. For a lamp to light there must be a complete circuit.

   i) State which lamp(s) are lit when S_1 and S_2 are closed (on) and S_3 open (off).   *(1 mark)*

   ii) State which lamp(s) are lit when S_3 is closed (on) and S_1 and S_2 open (off).   *(1 mark)*

2   The diagram shows part of a mains lighting circuit protected by a fuse in the mains fuse box (consumer unit). A, B, C and D are lamps in the circuit. The table gives information about each lamp.

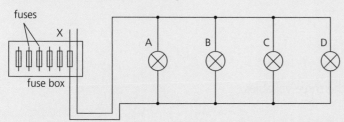

Lamp	Power (W)	Current (A)
A	40	0.17
B	60	0.26
C	40	0.17
D	60	0.26

a) When working normally, calculate how much current is flowing through the fuse at X.   *(1 mark)*

b) Add the following to the circuit diagram:

   i) a switch labelled S_1 which controls lamp A only

   ii) a switch labelled S_2 which controls lamps C and D only.   *(2 marks)*

Go online for answers

Simple electrical circuits 2

Investigating current and voltage

Revised

The circuit diagram shows a variable resistor connected in series with a fixed resistor. The resistance of the variable resistor can be changed, in order to vary the current through, and the voltage across, the fixed resistor. The fixed resistor could be replaced by any component, such as a filament lamp, to investigate how the current and voltage vary for the component.

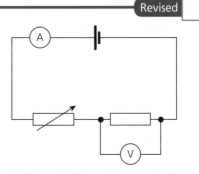

↑ The variable resistor controls the current through and voltage across a fixed resistor

Voltage–current relationships

The graphs below show the voltage–current relationships for a fixed resistor and a filament lamp.

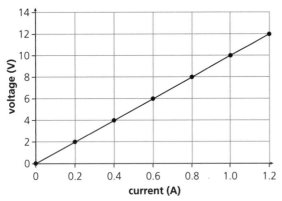
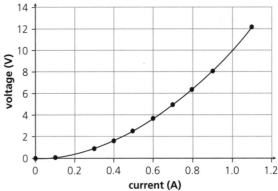

↑ Voltage against current for a 10 Ω fixed resistor (left) and a filament lamp (right)

- For fixed resistors (and wires at constant temperature), voltage and current are **proportional** to each other – doubling the current will double the voltage. The graph is linear (a straight line). A bigger resistance will give a bigger slope.

- For components such as filament lamps, the resistance changes with current. The resistance of a filament lamp increases with current, so the slope of the voltage–current graph increases.

The current, voltage and resistance of electrical and electronic components are related to each other. The physicist Georg Ohm investigated this in 1827. We summarise his findings using the equation:

$$\text{current, } I \text{ (amps)} = \frac{\text{voltage, } V \text{ (volts)}}{\text{resistance, } R \text{ (ohms)}}$$

$$I = \frac{V}{R}$$

This equation can be used to calculate any one of the three variables, provided that we know the other two.

Examples

1 A 20 Ω (ohm) fixed resistor has a voltage of 12 V across it. Calculate the current through it.

$$I = \frac{V}{R} = \frac{12}{20} = 0.6 \, A$$

2 Calculate the resistance of a filament lamp operating at 6 V with a current of 0.3 A through it.

$$I = \frac{V}{R} \quad \text{so } R = \frac{V}{I} = \frac{6}{0.3} = 20 \, \Omega$$

The rate of transfer of electrical energy by a device is the electrical **power**, P, measured in watts, W. It can be calculated using the equation:

$P = VI$

or the equation:

$P = I^2R$

Examples

3 Calculate the power of a filament lamp operating at a voltage of 12 V and a current of 0.5 A.

$P = VI = 12 \times 0.5 = 6\,W$

4 A fixed resistor with a resistance of 25 Ω has a current of 0.8 A through it. Calculate the power of the fixed resistor.

$P = I^2R = 0.8^2 \times 25 = 16\,W$

> **Examiner tip**
>
> Often an equation is given to you in an exam question, but sometimes you are asked to find a suitable equation from the formula sheet, which will be on the inside cover of the exam paper. On the Higher-Tier paper you may also need to rearrange an equation, so you need to practise this skill.

3 The circuit shows an ammeter A and a voltmeter V connected to a power supply and a resistance wire XY. A connector S allows the length of wire in the circuit to be changed.

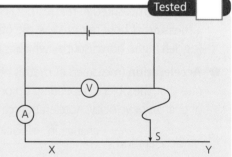

a) With S in the position shown, the voltmeter reads 6 V and the ammeter 1.2 A. State a suitable equation from the equations list on page 110 that could be used to calculate the resistance of the wire between X and S, and then use the equation and the data to calculate this. *(3 marks)*

b) The connector S is moved towards Y. State the effect, if any, this would have on:

i) the resistance in the circuit

ii) the ammeter reading.

4 The circuit shown is used to investigate how the resistance of a lamp changes.

a) Explain how component X allows a set of results to be obtained. *(2 marks)*

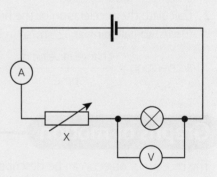

b) The results obtained are used to plot the graph shown.

i) Write down in words an equation from the equations list on page 111 and use it to calculate the resistance of the lamp when the voltage across it is 4 V. *(4 marks)*

ii) Use the graph and a suitable equation from the equations list on page 111 to calculate the power of the lamp when the voltage across it is 4 V. *(3 marks)*

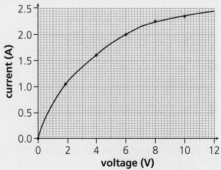

Go online for answers

Online

Distance, speed and acceleration

Describing motion

The motion of an object can be described using the following quantities:

● **Distance** (measured in metres, m): how far the object travels, or how far away the object is from a fixed point.

● **Time** (measured in seconds, s): the time interval between two events or the time since the start of the motion.

● **Speed** (measured in metres per second, m/s): a measure of how fast or slow the object is moving. The speed of the object can be calculated using the equation:

$$\text{speed} = \frac{\text{distance}}{\text{time}}$$

● **Velocity** (measured in metres per second, m/s, in a given direction): a measure of how fast or slow the object is moving in a given direction (e.g. left/right, north/south), which is the speed in a given direction.

● **Acceleration** (measured in metres per second per second, m/s²): the rate that the object is speeding up or slowing down, which is the rate of change of velocity. Acceleration can be calculated using the equation:

$$\text{acceleration} = \frac{\text{change in velocity}}{\text{time}}$$

Examples

1 Calculate the speed of a horse that gallops 200 m in 16 s.

$$\text{speed} = \frac{\text{distance}}{\text{time}} = \frac{200}{16} = 12.5 \, \text{m/s}$$

2 Calculate the acceleration of the horse if it takes 5 s to get from rest (0 m/s) to galloping at 12.5 m/s.

$$\text{acceleration} = \frac{\text{change in velocity}}{\text{time}} = \frac{(12.5 - 0)}{5} = \frac{12.5}{5} = 2.5 \, \text{m/s}^2$$

> **Examiner tip**
>
> You need to be very careful when you are analysing and extracting information from a graph in a question. Many students make mistakes by reading the axes incorrectly. A good technique to help you measure quantities from graphs is to use a sharp pencil and a ruler to draw thin guidelines onto the axes at the places where you need to take a reading.

Graphs of motion

The motion of objects can be described and analysed using graphs of motion. There are two types of motion graph: **distance–time graphs** and **velocity–time graphs**.

Distance–time graphs

● A distance–time graph allows us to measure the speed of a moving object.

● The graph shows an object moving away from a starting point at a constant speed of 6 m/s.

● Stationary objects are represented by straight horizontal lines.

● The slope or **gradient** of a distance–time graph is the speed of the object.

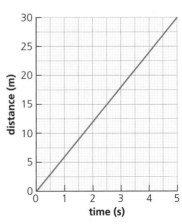

↑ **Distance–time graph**

Velocity–time graphs

A velocity–time graph gives us more information than a distance–time graph. The graph here shows an object:

● stationary for 2 seconds

● accelerating at 3 m/s² for 2 seconds

● moving at a constant velocity of 6 m/s for 6 s.

The slope or gradient of a velocity–time graph is the **acceleration** of the object.

The distance travelled by the object is the area under the velocity–time graph (in this case 42 m).

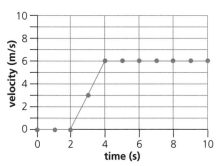

⬆ Velocity–time graph

5 During road tests, three cars are tested to find out how long they take to accelerate from 0 to 60 mph (27 m/s). The results are shown in the table.

    a) State which car, W, X or Y, has the smallest acceleration. *(1 mark)*

    b) A velocity of 60 mph is the same as a velocity of 27 m/s. Use a suitable equation from the equation list on page 110 to calculate the acceleration of car Y during the test in m/s². *(3 marks)*

Car	Time to reach 60 mph from rest/s
W	5
X	8
Y	9

6 A theme park ride involves a group of people being lifted in a carriage and then dropped from a height. The graph shows the motion of such a ride.

    a) Describe the motion of the carriage in the first 20 s. *(1 mark)*

    b) Select a suitable equation from the equation list on page 110 to find the acceleration of the carriage between 30 s and 35 s. *(2 marks)*

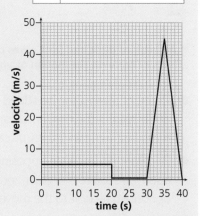

7 A car overtakes a lorry. In doing so, the car accelerates and, after overtaking safely, returns to its original speed. The graph represents the motion of the car when overtaking the lorry.

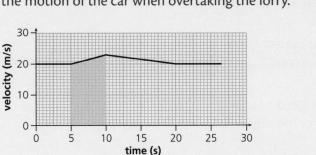

    a) Write down an equation from the equation list on page 110 and then use it, together with data from the graph, to calculate the acceleration of the car during overtaking. *(4 marks)*

    b) Describe clearly what the shaded area of the graph represents. *(2 marks)*

    c) Use the data from the graph to calculate the distance travelled between 10 s and 20 s. *(3 marks)*

The effect of forces 1

Unbalanced forces on an object can cause the object to change its:

- speed (by accelerating or decelerating)
- direction of movement
- shape (by being deformed).

Investigating forces and motion

The effect of a resultant horizontal force on an object free to move can be investigated using the apparatus shown.

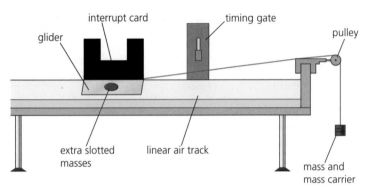

↑ **A linear air track and light gates can be used to investigate the effects of force on the motion of an object**

- Different masses can be added to the falling mass carrier, increasing or decreasing the horizontal force. The acceleration of the glider is measured using an 'interrupt card' with two sections as shown.
- Deceleration under an opposing force can be investigated by adding a stiff card sail to the glider and using a drinking straw to blow in the opposite direction to the movement of the glider.
- Collisions can be investigated by adding rubber band 'buffers' to the glider and the stop-ends of the air track, or having a second glider moving in the opposite direction.
- The effect of forces on changing shape can be investigated by adding different types of 'crumple zone' to either the glider or the stop-ends of the air track.

Inertia

The mass of an object dictates how easy (or difficult) it is to get the object moving or to change its motion. This property is called **inertia**, defined as the resistance of any object to a change in its state of motion or rest.

Very massive objects, such as the International Space Station, have very large inertia. Altering their motion takes a very large force.

Newton's first law

In 1687 Isaac Newton realised the link between the motion of an object and the force on it. He summarised this in his first law of motion.

On Earth it is very difficult to observe Newton's first law, because **friction** always acts to oppose the motion of an object.

'An object at rest stays at rest, or an object in motion stays in motion with the same speed and in the same direction, unless acted upon by an unbalanced force.'

↑ **Newton's first law of motion**

Another way to link force and motion is to think of both the mass and the velocity of a moving object. Objects that require a large force to stop either have very large mass (inertia) or are moving at very high velocity. **Momentum** is the name given to the product of the mass and velocity of an object. So objects with a large momentum require a large force to alter their motion.

momentum p (kg m/s) = mass m (kg) × velocity v (m/s)

$p = mv$

Examples

1. A rifle fires a bullet of mass 0.005 g (5×10^{-6} kg) with a velocity of 400 m/s. Calculate the momentum of the bullet.

   $p = mv = 5 \times 10^{-6} \times 400 = 2 \times 10^{-3}$ kg m/s

2. The rifle has a mass of 5 kg and recoils with the same momentum. Calculate the recoil velocity of the rifle.

   $p = mv$ so $v = \dfrac{p}{m} = \dfrac{(2 \times 10^{-3})}{5} = 4 \times 10^{-4}$ m/s

> **Examiner tip**
>
> When using an equation to calculate values such as momentum, you need to be careful about which numbers you use in the equation. In the exam, once you have found and written down the equation, you could highlight the quantity in the equation and the appropriate number in the question.

Check your understanding   Tested

8. A car is stopped at traffic lights. At time 0 seconds, the lights change to green. After the car speeds up it travels around a bend.

   a) How long does it take the driver to react when the lights change to green?   *(1 mark)*

   b) At what time did the speed reach 6.0 m/s?   *(1 mark)*

   c) As the car goes around the bend, one of the following quantities changes. Which one changes?   *(1 mark)*

   speed   velocity   size of the driving force

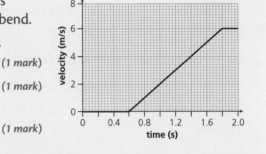

9. A gun fires a bullet of mass 0.01 kg, with a speed of 1000 m/s, at a target. The bullet passes straight through the target, losing some momentum as it does so, before emerging with a velocity v.

   a) i) State and use an equation from the equation list on page 110 to calculate the momentum of the bullet **before** passing through the target.   *(2 marks)*

   ii) The bullet loses 9 kg m/s of momentum passing through the target. Calculate the momentum of the bullet as it emerges from the target.   *(1 mark)*

   iii) The emerging bullet has the same mass as it did before entering the target. Use your answer to **(ii)** to calculate the velocity of the bullet as it emerges from the target.   *(2 marks)*

   b) The gun has a mass of 1.25 kg. When the bullet is fired, the gun recoils with the same value of momentum as the fired bullet (your answer to **(a)(i)**). Use this information to calculate the recoil velocity of the rifle.   *(2 marks)*

Go online for answers   Online

The effect of forces 2

Resultant force

When several forces act on an object at the same time, they either cancel each other out (balanced forces), or they combine together to produce a **resultant** (unbalanced) force.

The diagram shows two forces acting on a lorry. The two forces combine to produce a single resultant force, in the direction of motion, of 800 N.

● A resultant force acting on an object causes a change in its motion. (The lorry will accelerate.)

● Balanced forces cause an object to remain stationary or move at constant speed.

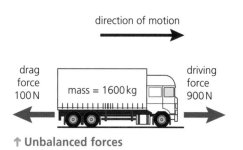

↑ **Unbalanced forces**

Experiments show us that as the resultant force on an object increases, so does the size of the acceleration. If we double the resultant force, then the acceleration doubles. The resultant force and the acceleration are **proportional** to each other.

When a graph of resultant force against acceleration is analysed further, we find that the gradient of the line is equal to the mass of the object.

Expressing this as a word equation, we can say:

resultant force, F (N) = mass, m (kg) × acceleration, a (m/s^2)

$F = ma$

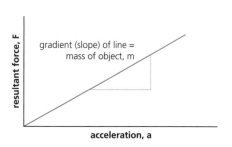

↑ **A graph of resultant force against acceleration is a straight line**

This equation is one form of **Newton's second law**. It can also be written as:

$$\text{resultant force, } F \text{ (N)} = \frac{\text{change in momentum, } \Delta p \text{ (kg m/s)}}{\text{time for change, } t \text{ (s)}}$$

$F = \Delta p/t$

Examples

1 The lorry starts at rest and accelerates to 20 m/s in 40 s. Calculate its change in momentum.

Change in momentum = momentum of lorry at 20 m/s − momentum of lorry at 0 m/s

Momentum of lorry at 20 m/s = mass × velocity = 1600 × 20 = 32 000 kg m/s

Change in momentum = 32 000 − 0 = 32 000 kg m/s

2 Use the answer to Example 1 to calculate the resultant force on the lorry.

$$F = \frac{\Delta p}{t} = \frac{32\,000}{40} = 800 \text{ N}$$

3 The lorry in the diagram has a mass of 1600 kg. Calculate its acceleration.

Resultant force, $F = 800$ N

$$F = ma \qquad \text{so } a = \frac{F}{m} = \frac{800}{1600} = 0.5 \text{ m/s}^2$$

Examiner tip

Questions involving selection of answers from a list, as in Question **10** opposite, can appear straightforward. But they can easily catch people out! Read the question **really** carefully – at least twice, and make sure that the answer you are selecting actually answers the question being asked. A good technique is to highlight the key words in the question, for example 'speeds up' and 'air resistance' in Question **10 (a)**.

Falling objects

The **mass** of an object is a measure of how much matter (stuff) there is in the object. Mass, m, is measured in kilograms, kg. The **weight** of an object is the **force of gravity** acting on the object's mass. Weight is measured in newtons, N.

On the surface of the Earth the weight of a 1 kg object is approximately 10 N. The weight of any object on the Earth's surface can be calculated by multiplying its mass, in kg, by 10. The weight of the 1600 kg lorry in the example is therefore 16 000 N.

As an object, such as a parachutist, falls, the weight remains constant. Initially the only (resultant) force on the parachutist is her weight, so she accelerates downwards. As she speeds up, the force of **air resistance** acting upwards on her increases. Eventually it is equal and opposite to her weight – the two forces are equal in size but acting in opposite directions – they are balanced. The parachutist continues to fall, but at a constant (**terminal**) speed.

air resistance

weight

↑ **Balanced forces mean a moving object travels at constant speed**

Check your understanding

10 The diagram above shows two forces acting on a skydiver. Choose the correct phrase in each set of brackets in the following.

  a) When the skydiver speeds up, the air resistance is **(bigger than/equal to/smaller than)** the weight. *(1 mark)*

  b) When the skydiver falls at the terminal speed, the air resistance is **(bigger than/equal to/smaller than)** the weight. *(1 mark)*

  c) When the parachute is opened, the air resistance **(gets bigger/stays the same/gets smaller)** and the skydiver **(goes back up/stays in the same place/continues to fall)**. *(2 marks)*

11 The diagram shows a test rocket on its launch pad.

The rocket is powered by three engines, each of which produces a thrust of 2000 N. The mass of the rocket and its fuel is 500 kg, so that its weight is 5000 N.

  a) When the engines are fired:

    i) calculate the total thrust on the rocket *(1 mark)*

    ii) explain why the rocket moves upwards *(1 mark)*

    iii) calculate the resultant force on the rocket *(1 mark)*

    iv) select and use a suitable equation from the equation list on page 111 to calculate the take-off acceleration of the rocket. *(3 marks)*

  b) After 2 s, the rocket engines have used up 20 kg of fuel. Assuming that the thrust of the engines is constant, calculate:

    i) the mass of the rocket and fuel after 2 s *(1 mark)*

    ii) the resultant force in newtons on the rocket after 2 s *(1 mark)*

    iii) the acceleration of the rocket after 2 s. *(1 mark)*

  c) Assuming that the thrust of the engines is constant, explain why the acceleration of the rocket will continue to increase for as long as the engines are fired. *(2 marks)*

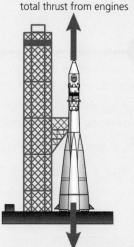
total thrust from engines

weight of rocket plus fuel

Go online for answers

Interactions between objects 1

Interaction pairs

Forces between two objects always act in pairs. The force on one object is called the **action** force; the force on the other object is called the **reaction** force. Together they form an **interaction pair**. The action force and the reaction force are equal and opposite. But they do not cancel each other out because they act on different objects.

This is known as Newton's third law:

'For every action force, there is an equal and opposite reaction force.'

Example

1   If some rugby players are practising scrummaging against a static scrum-machine and are pushing with a combined force of 500 N (the action force), then the scrum-machine exerts a reaction force on the players of 500 N in the opposite direction.

Some forces (like those involved in scrummaging) are **contact forces**: the two objects must come into contact with each other to exert the force. Other forces are **'action at a distance' forces**, such as gravity, or the forces exerted by electric and magnetic fields.

When considering interaction pairs you need to remember that:

1   The two forces in the pair act on different objects.

2   The two forces are equal in size, but act in opposite directions.

3   The two forces are always the same type, for example contact forces or gravitational forces.

action force of players on machine

reaction force of machine on players

↑ **The action and reaction forces are equal and opposite**

> ### Examiner tip
> When a diagram is given that shows several interaction pairs of forces, it is a good idea to highlight the individual pairs. This makes it easier to analyse them under the pressure of the exam.

Work

When a force causes an object to move, or acts on a moving object, energy is transferred. The force moves through a distance and energy is transferred as **work**, measured in joules, J.

The amount of work done is calculated by:

work = force × distance moved in the direction of the force

$W = Fd$

Example

2   In rugby, the players lifting the jumper in a lineout exert an upward force, moving the jumper through a distance. If the lifting force is 1000 N and the player is lifted through 1.5 m then the work done is:

$W = Fd = 1000 \times 1.5 = 1500\,J$

The work done is **a measure** of the energy transferred. But the work done only equals the total energy transferred **if no energy is lost as heat to the surroundings** (by air resistance or friction).

force, F

distance moved, d

↑ **The force F moves through a distance d**

Friction

Friction is a force that always opposes the motion of objects. If a scrum-machine is being pushed along the grass by a pack of forwards, then the friction between the machine and the grass will act in the opposite direction. The friction between the two surfaces converts the kinetic energy of the motion into heat. The size of the force of friction depends upon:

- the weight of the object in contact with the surface
- the roughness of the surfaces in contact
- the area in contact.

Examiner tip

When doing calculations involving work done, the distance involved is always the distance that the force moves through. In Question **13** below, there are two distances – make sure that you use the correct distance for each force.

Check your understanding

12 The diagram shows a low-loader lorry winching a car up a ramp.

The winch of the lorry does 2450 J of work in lifting the car and 350 J of work against friction whilst pulling the car up the 3.5 m ramp.

a) Calculate the total work done in raising the car on to the back of the lorry. *(1 mark)*

b) Select a suitable equation from the list on page 111 to find the force *F*. *(3 marks)*

13 The diagram shows a winch at Y which is used to pull a yacht at X 50 m up a slipway through a vertical height of 4 m.

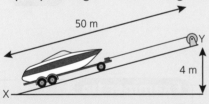

a) The weight of the yacht is 15 000 N, and is lifted through the vertical height of 4 m. Write down a suitable equation from the list on page 110 and use it to calculate the work done against gravity, lifting the yacht through 4 m. *(2 marks)*

b) A frictional force of 1000 N acts on the yacht as it is pulled up the 50 m slipway. Use your equation from **(a)** to calculate the work done against this frictional force. *(1 mark)*

c) i) Hence calculate the total amount of work done by the winch in pulling the yacht up the slipway. *(1 mark)*

ii) Calculate the force that must be applied by the winch in pulling the yacht up the slipway. *(2 marks)*

Go online for answers

Interactions between objects 2

Gravitational potential energy
Revised

When an object such as a ball is thrown or kicked vertically, the mass of the ball, m, is moved against the Earth's gravitational field strength, g, through a change in height, h, and it gains **gravitational potential energy**, PE.

$$\text{gravitational potential energy} = \text{mass } m \text{ (kg)} \times \text{gravitational field strength } g \text{ (N/kg)} \times \text{change in height } h \text{ (m)}$$

$PE = mgh$

Example

1 Calculate the gravitational potential energy of a 0.44 kg rugby ball kicked vertically upwards to a height of 20 m. The gravitational field strength $g = 10$ N/kg.

   $PE = mgh = 0.44 \times 10 \times 20 = 88\,J$

2 A rugby player of mass 100 kg is lifted in a lineout, gaining 1500 J of gravitational potential energy. Calculate the height he is lifted. The gravitational field strength g = 10 N/kg

   $PE = mgh$ so $h = \dfrac{PE}{mg} = \dfrac{1500}{100 \times 10} = 1.5\,m$

Kinetic energy
Revised

When players run with a ball, the chemical energy from their food converts in their muscles to **kinetic energy**, KE (movement energy). We can calculate the kinetic energy of any moving object using the equation:

kinetic energy (J) = ½ × mass m (kg) × (velocity v)² (m/s)²

$KE = \frac{1}{2}mv^2$

Example

3 A rugby player can run with a rugby ball with a mean velocity of about 10 m/s. He has a mass of 80 kg. When running at 10 m/s, what is his kinetic energy?

   $KE = \frac{1}{2}mv^2 = 0.5 \times 80 \times 10^2 = 4000\,J$

4 A rugby ball of mass 0.44 kg is passed from one player to another with a kinetic energy of 2 J. Calculate the mean velocity of the ball.

   $KE = \frac{1}{2}mv^2$

   so $v = \sqrt{\dfrac{2KE}{m}} = \sqrt{\dfrac{2 \times 2}{0.44}} = 3\,m/s$

> **Examiner tip**
>
> The equation for kinetic energy is unusual in that it involves the square of the velocity, v^2. A common mistake is to forget to square the velocity. Square the velocity first, then multiply by the mass and 0.5.

When objects such as rugby balls move, there is an interplay of gravitational potential energy and kinetic energy. The total energy of the ball stays constant, assuming that there is no energy lost through air resistance or friction.

total energy = gravitational potential energy + kinetic energy

total energy = PE + KE

The diagram shows the energy transformations during the flight of a ball after kicking upwards.

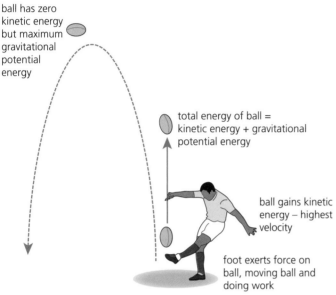

ball has zero kinetic energy but maximum gravitational potential energy

total energy of ball = kinetic energy + gravitational potential energy

ball gains kinetic energy – highest velocity

foot exerts force on ball, moving ball and doing work

⬆ **The interaction of kinetic energy and gravitational potential energy on kicking a ball up**

Examiner tip

Questions involving the interaction of gravitational potential energy and kinetic energy often come up in exams. Typically, they involve fairground rides, skiers, or bicycles going down slopes. You should try as many of these types of question as you can to practise exchanging the two types of energy and doing the calculations.

Check your understanding

14 A lift takes people up to a jump platform in a bungee tower. The jump platform is 55 m above the ground.

   a) The lift takes a 60 kg person from the ground to the jump platform. Write down an equation as it appears in the list on page 111, and use it to find the increase in gravitational potential energy of the person. (Gravitational field strength = 10 N/kg) *(3 marks)*

   b) The bungee jumper has a kinetic energy of 18 000 J when he is falling at maximum speed.

     i) What is his potential energy when he reaches his maximum speed? *(1 mark)*

     ii) Write down an equation as it appears in the list on page 111 and use it to find his maximum speed. *(3 marks)*

   c) Explain in terms of named forces why the speed increases before the bungee rope starts to stretch. *(2 marks)*

   d) The bungee rope stretches and stops the jumper just at ground level, storing the bungee jumper's energy in the rope. Give the values at this point of:

     i) his kinetic energy *(1 mark)*

     ii) his gravitational potential energy *(1 mark)*

     iii) the energy stored in the bungee rope. *(1 mark)*

Go online for answers

Online

Cars, the Highway Code and collisions

Stopping distance

Revised

Vehicles do not stop instantaneously – there is a time delay between the driver seeing the need to stop, such as a potential hazard, and the vehicle stopping. During this time, the vehicle is still travelling at speed so the car travels through a distance. The total **stopping distance** of a vehicle is made up of the 'thinking distance' and the 'braking distance'.

- **Thinking distance** is the distance the vehicle travels while the driver sees the hazard, thinks about braking and then actually reacts to put the brakes on.

- **Braking distance** is the distance that the vehicle moves while the brakes are being applied and the vehicle is decelerating to 0 m/s.

  total stopping distance = thinking distance + braking distance

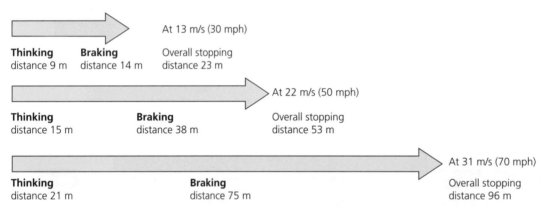

At 13 m/s (30 mph)

Thinking distance 9 m   **Braking** distance 14 m   Overall stopping distance 23 m

At 22 m/s (50 mph)

Thinking distance 15 m   **Braking** distance 38 m   Overall stopping distance 53 m

At 31 m/s (70 mph)

Thinking distance 21 m   **Braking** distance 75 m   Overall stopping distance 96 m

↑ **Thinking distance and braking distance at different speeds (from the Highway Code)**

Factors affecting stopping distance

Revised

Thinking distance depends on several different factors, including:

- the velocity of the car
- the **reaction time** of the driver (which depends on tiredness, alcohol use etc.)
- the driver may be distracted
- the driver may have been using a mobile phone.

The braking distance also depends on several factors:

- the velocity of the car
- the mass of the car
- the condition of the brakes
- the condition of the tyres
- the condition of the road surface
- the weather.

Stopping safely

When a car stops very quickly, for example in a collision, in order to minimise the injuries to the occupants the key factor to reduce is the forces that act on them. Car manufacturers have built safety systems into modern cars to reduce these forces: seat belts, air bags and crumple zones.

Newton's second law (page 90) is:

$$\text{resultant force, } F \text{ (N)} = \frac{\text{change in momentum, } \Delta p \text{ (kg m/s)}}{\text{time for change, } t \text{ (s)}}$$

$$F = \Delta p / t$$

There are two ways of reducing the force:

1 Reduce the speed of the collision, so reducing the change of momentum.

2 Increase the time for the collision.

All three safety systems listed above work by increasing the time of the collision – by allowing something to be deformed during the collision. Seat belts stretch; airbags slowly deflate; crumple zones crumple in on themselves.

> ### Examiner tip
>
> Question **16 b)** below is an example of a question that asks you to choose between two factors, both of which are correct. You get **no** marks for the choice – the marks are awarded for your explanations. You could write 'This is the case... because...'.

Check your understanding

15 The overall stopping distance of a car is made up of two parts: thinking distance and braking distance. At a speed of 20 m/s the Highway Code states that a car has a **thinking distance of 12 m** and a **braking distance of 40 m**.

a) Use a suitable equation from the list on page 110 to find the **thinking time** for a driver. *(2 marks)*

b) Complete the table below. Some boxes have been completed for you. *(3 marks)*

Condition	Effect on thinking distance	Effect on braking distance	Effect on overall stopping distance
Poor brakes	No change	Increases	Increases
Driver under the influence of alcohol			Increases
Driver drives at a lower speed	Decreases		
Wet road		Increases	

16 A car safety engineer is checking the design for a crumple zone in a car. According to the computer models, the crumple zone produces a force of 480 000 N when it is being compressed in a front collision. The car has a mass of 1200 kg, including passengers. The design requirement for the maximum crumple distance of the crumple zone is 0.6 m.

a) The engineer uses ideas of kinetic energy and work to show that the crumple distance at 25 m/s is almost 0.8 m. Explain clearly and use calculations to show how she could arrive at this figure. *(6 marks QWC)*

b) The figure of 0.8 m is too long, so she suggests two possible changes to the design of the car:

A make the crumple zone stiffer, i.e. it exerts a bigger force

B make the car lighter.

Choose **one** of these suggestions and explain how it would result in a shorter stopping distance. *(2 marks)*

Go online for answers

Radioactive decay

Nuclear radiation
Revised

Some types of atom are **radioactive**. This means that the nucleus of the atom is **unstable** and can break apart, emitting **ionising radiation** in the form of **alpha** (α), **beta** (β) or **gamma** (γ) radiation.

● Alpha particles are helium nuclei. They are the most ionising and the least penetrating type of nuclear radiation – they are absorbed by a thin sheet of paper or by skin.

● Beta particles are high-energy electrons. They have medium ionising ability and are absorbed by a few millimetres of aluminium or perspex plastic.

● Gamma rays are high-energy electromagnetic waves. They are the least ionising and the most penetrating, able to travel through several centimetres of lead.

Inside the nucleus
Revised

The nucleus of an atom contains positively charged particles, **protons**, and neutral particles, **neutrons**.

The number of protons in the nucleus is called the **proton number**, Z; the number of protons plus the number of neutrons is called the **nucleon number**, A.

The values of Z and A are often shown using the $^{A}_{Z}X$ notation, where X is the chemical symbol for the atom in question.

For example, 52.4% of all naturally occurring lead atoms have nuclei made up of 82 protons and 126 neutrons, a total of 208 nucleons, i.e. $^{208}_{82}Pb$.

Lead also has other **isotopes** – nuclei with the same number of protons, but different numbers of neutrons. The different isotopes are often written as Pb-208, Pb-207, etc., where the number refers to the nucleon number.

Stability of the nucleus
Revised

In a stable atom there is an optimum balance between the number of protons and the number of neutrons in the nucleus. But some isotopes can have too few or too many neutrons, causing an imbalance and making the nucleus unstable and radioactive. For example:

● the lead isotope Pb-181 has only 99 neutrons and is an alpha particle emitter

● the lead isotope Pb-214 has 132 neutrons and is a beta emitter.

The nucleus becomes more stable by emitting alpha or beta particles, restoring the optimum balance of protons and neutrons, and sometimes emitting gamma radiation too.

Nuclear equations

Revised

The $^A_Z X$ notation can be used to represent the decay of radioactive nuclei in a nuclear equation. Alpha particles are written as ^4_2He because they consist of two protons and two neutrons, like a helium nucleus. Beta particles are written as $^0_{-1}e$, because they are electrons.

Alpha decay

The nuclear decay equation for the alpha decay of lead-181 is:

$$^{181}_{82}Pb \longrightarrow {}^4_2He + {}^{177}_{80}Hg$$

The lead-181 nucleus emits an alpha particle, losing 4 nucleons (2 protons + 2 neutrons), forming mercury-177.

Beta decay

The nuclear decay equation for the beta decay of lead-214 is:

$$^{214}_{82}Pb \longrightarrow {}^0_{-1}e + {}^{214}_{83}Bi$$

The lead-214 nucleus emits a beta particle (electron). The nucleon number stays the same, but the proton number goes up by one, forming bismuth-214.

Examiner tip

All nuclear equations must balance: the total proton number on each side must be the same, and the total nucleon number on each side must be the same.

Examiner tip

Question **17** is an example of a question containing complex tables. In the exam you must spend time studying tables very carefully. Re-read the column and row headings and make sure that you know exactly what data is being given to you.

Check your understanding

Tested

17 Some radioactive elements emit more than one type of radiation.

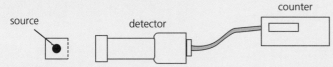

The above apparatus was used to investigate the radiation emitted from three sources, A, B and C. The sources were always placed at the same position, close to the detector. The table below shows the mean counts per minute obtained when different materials were placed between the sources and the detector. All the readings have been corrected for background radiation.

Source	Mean counts/min with nothing between source and detector	Mean counts/min with thin paper in the way	Mean counts/min with 3 mm of aluminium in the way	Mean counts/min with 2 cm of lead in the way
A	256	256	256	85
B	135	80	80	0
C	310	310	188	0

a) How can you tell that source A is emitting gamma (γ) radiation? *(1 mark)*

b) Which source, A, B or C, emits alpha (α) particles? Give a reason for your answer. *(2 marks)*

c) The beta radiation source contains atoms of strontium-90, $^{90}_{38}Sr$.

i) Explain what happens to a Sr-90 atom when it decays. *(2 marks)*

ii) The elements nearest to strontium in the Periodic Table are shown below.

Element	Krypton	Rubidium	Strontium	Yttrium	Zirconium
Symbol	Kr	Rb	Sr	Y	Zr
Proton number	36	37	38	39	40

Use the information in the table to determine the daughter nucleus produced when Sr-90 decays by beta emission. *(3 marks)*

Go online for answers

Online

Half-life and uses of nuclear radiation

Radioactive decay and half-life

The unit of radioactive decay activity is the **becquerel**, Bq. An activity of 1 Bq is equivalent to 1 radioactive decay per second.

Radioactive materials decay in a very predictable way. The graph below shows a typical radioactive **decay curve**, for the decay of iridium-192.

The initial activity of the sample is 500 Bq. After 74 days the activity has fallen to 250 Bq – half the original amount. This time is called the **half-life** of iridium-192. After another 74 days, the activity has fallen to 125 Bq – half of 250 Bq – after each half-life the activity halves.

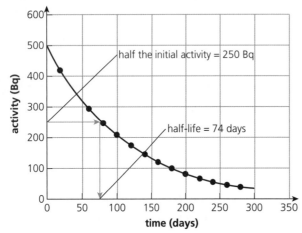

↑ **Radioactive decay graph of iridium-192**

> **Examiner tip**
>
> The decay of every radioactive material follows the same pattern. The activities and the half-lives may be very different, but the shape of the decay curve is always the same.

Half-lives range from the very short (e.g. 0.000 000 000 000 000 001 s) to the very long (e.g. 1 000 000 000 000 000 000 000 years) – longer than the age of the Universe.

The half-life of a particular radioactive material is fixed – it depends only on the type of atom. This makes it easy to work out how much radioactive activity there will be some time in the future, or at some time in the past.

Example

An iridium-192 source has a half-life of 74 days and an initial activity of 1200 Bq. What will the activity of the iridium source be after 222 days?

Number of half-lives in 222 days $= \dfrac{222}{74} = 3$ half-lives

After 1 half-life (74 days) the activity will be $\dfrac{1200}{2} = 600$ Bq.

After the second half-life (148 days), the activity will be $\dfrac{600}{2} = 300$ Bq.

After the third half-life (222 days), the activity will be $\dfrac{300}{2} = 150$ Bq.

The uses of radioactive materials depend on their properties, in particular their:

● half-life

● penetrating power and ionising power.

In medicine, radioactive materials are used in two main ways: in **imaging** and in **therapy** (treatment).

Radio-imaging

The radioactive material is injected into the body, it makes its way to the particular place of interest to the doctors and it emits gamma rays, which can be detected outside of the body. Gamma emitters are used, such as technetium-99 with a half-life of six hours. This will only remain radioactive for 30 hours or so (about 5 half-lives). Gamma rays cause few problems to the body as they pass straight through and are very weak ionisers.

Radiotherapy

This involves the use of radioactive materials to kill affected (usually cancerous) cells. Beta radiation may be used, as this has a short range in flesh so that it only damages the cells close to the target area. The half-life chosen is typically a few days, but depends on the dose required – longer half-lives will deliver higher doses.

> **Examiner tip**
>
> Question **19** below involves drawing a decay graph. When you have to draw a graph in an exam, you are nearly always given the axes and grid. The most important thing is to plot the points accurately and correctly and draw a best-fit curve – always check your graph two or three times after you have plotted it, and use pencil so that you can rub it out if you make a mistake.

18 To study blood flow a doctor injects some technetium-99 (Tc-99) into a patient. The gamma radiation given out by the Tc-99 atoms is detected using a gamma camera outside the patient's body. The graph shows how the count rate from a sample of Tc-99 changes with time.

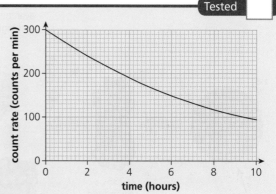

a) i) How many hours does it take for the count rate to fall from 300 counts per minute to 150 counts per minute? *(1 mark)*

ii) What is the half-life of Tc-99? *(1 mark)*

iii) How long will it take for the count rate to fall from 300 to 75 counts per minute? *(1 mark)*

b) Explain why an alpha-emitting source would be unsuitable to study blood flow. *(2 marks)*

19 a) Carbon-14 has a half-life of 5700 years. Sketch a graph of activity against time, showing the decay of carbon-14 from an initial activity of 64 counts per minute. *(3 marks)*

b) While trees are alive they absorb and emit carbon-14 (in the form of carbon dioxide) so that the amount of carbon-14 in them remains constant.

i) What happens to the amount of carbon-14 in a tree after it dies? *(1 mark)*

ii) A sample of wood from an ancient dwelling gives 36 counts per minute. A similar sample of living wood has 64 counts per minute. From your graph, deduce the age of the dwelling. (Show on your graph how you obtained your answer.) *(2 marks)*

Go online for answers

Online

Fission and fusion

Nuclear fission

The stability of an atomic nucleus is dictated by the number of protons and neutrons within the nucleus. Heavy nuclei (generally with atomic numbers above 27 (iron, Fe)) tend to have a large number of neutrons compared to the number of protons. This makes them unstable and they can break apart – a process called **nuclear fission**.

Nuclear fission releases energy. On a large scale huge amounts of energy can be produced in a controlled way in a **nuclear reactor**. The energy (in the form of heat) can be used to generate electricity – known as **nuclear power**.

Fission of 1 kg of nuclear fuel can produce 83 000 000 000 000 J of energy; by comparison, combustion of 1 kg of coal can produce 35 000 000 J.

In one type of nuclear reactor, uranium-235 nuclei are broken up into two **daughter nuclei** when bombarded by **slow moving neutrons**. The process produces two or three more neutrons, which in turn can induce the fission of other U-235 nuclei, and so on, starting a **chain reaction**.

We can represent one fission event by the nuclear equation:

$$^{235}_{92}U + {}^{1}_{0}n \longrightarrow {}^{144}_{56}Ba + {}^{89}_{36}Kr + 3{}^{1}_{0}n + \text{energy}$$

> ### Examiner tip
> Questions involving nuclear fission can be tricky. The number of neutrons produced when U-235 undergoes fission is not constant and varies between one and three. Always read the question carefully and study any fission diagrams or equations to make sure you are certain how many neutrons are produced.

fission yields fragments of intermediate mass, an average of 2.4 neutrons, and high kinetic energy

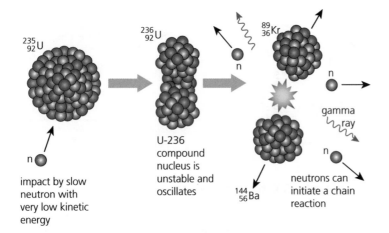

$^{235}_{92}U$

impact by slow neutron with very low kinetic energy

$^{236}_{92}U$

U-236 compound nucleus is unstable and oscillates

$^{89}_{36}Kr$

$^{144}_{56}Ba$

gamma ray

neutrons can initiate a chain reaction

↑ **Fission of uranium-235**

The daughter nuclei of fission reactions are themselves radioactive and decay by alpha, beta or gamma emission. They have wide-ranging but generally extremely long half-lives (typically hundreds of thousands of years) and they will remain dangerously radioactive for a very long time. This why some nuclear waste requires extremely secure long-term storage.

Controlling and containing the reaction

Fission only occurs if the bombarding neutrons are moving slowly enough. To initiate a chain reaction, the fast-moving neutrons released in the fission events need to be slowed down.

The fuel rods in the reactor are surrounded by a material called a **moderator** which slows the neutrons down. This is normally water (which also acts as the coolant and the mechanism of heat transfer for the reactor).

The chain reaction can be completely stopped, speeded up or slowed down by controlling the *number* of slow neutrons in the reactor. This is achieved by inserting neutron-absorbing **control rods** into spaces between the fuel rods.

A nuclear reactor core emits huge amounts of radioactivity and neutrons, and needs to be shielded from the environment. There is a thick metal casing around the reactor vessel and also a thick concrete containment structure surrounding that.

Nuclear fusion
Revised

The energy produced by our Sun is a result of nuclear reactions. In this case, the nuclear reaction involves the **fusion** (joining together) of nuclei.

In a prototype nuclear fusion reactor here on Earth, an ionised gas (**plasma**) of two isotopes of hydrogen: deuterium, ^2_1H and tritium, ^3_1H, are fused together at very high temperatures (many millions of degrees Celsius).

$$^2_1H + {}^3_1H \longrightarrow {}^4_2He + {}^1_0n$$

Fusion of 1 kg of hydrogen could produce over 7 times as much energy as fission of 1 kg of uranium-235.

The problem with designing nuclear fusion reactors is containing the high temperature plasma and also containing the radiation emitted during the process.

> **Examiner tip**
>
> Nuclear fission and fusion questions frequently involve completion of nuclear equations. These, like all nuclear equations, must balance: the total proton number on each side must be the same, and the total nucleon number on each side must be the same.

Check your understanding
Tested

20 The following equation shows a nuclear reaction.

$$^2_1H + {}^2_1H \longrightarrow {}^3_2He + {}^1_0n$$

This reaction only takes place if the particles on the left-hand side of the equation move very quickly towards each other. This needs a very high temperature. The reaction then releases a huge amount of energy.

a) Choose the correct word or words in the brackets of each sentence below.

   i) The particles that collide together in this reaction are atoms of
      (hydrogen, helium, oxygen). *(1 mark)*

   ii) This is an example of a **(fission, chain, fusion)** reaction. *(1 mark)*

b) Give **two** reasons why this reaction is very difficult to control. *(2 marks)*

21 In an uncontrolled nuclear fission reaction, when a slow-moving neutron strikes an atom of U (uranium), the atom splits. In this reaction two fast-moving neutrons are produced together with the radioactive fission fragments of Ba (barium) and Kr (krypton).

a) Write out and complete the nuclear equation for this reaction. *(2 marks)*

$$^{235}_{92}U + {}^1_0n \longrightarrow {}^{144}Ba + {}_{36}Kr + 2{}^1_0n$$

b) In a nuclear reactor, the fission reaction is controlled using control rods of boron steel, which readily absorbs neutrons, and a graphite moderator which improves the chances of uranium atoms splitting apart.

   i) State how the graphite moderator improves the possibility of fission of uranium. *(1 mark)*

   ii) Explain how the energy released from a nuclear reactor can be increased. *(1 mark)*

c) Outline the advantages of producing electricity from nuclear fusion rather than nuclear fission in the future. *(3 marks)*

Go online for answers — Online

Experimental design and mathematical skills

Questions about experimental design usually relate to the ideas of fair testing and validity. Mathematical skills tested include simple processes (addition, subtraction, multiplication and division), percentages, means, calculating rates and manipulating equations.

Experimental design   Revised ☐

Validity

- Valid tests are ones that provide information that can be used to support or contradict a hypothesis.

- In order to be valid, tests must be fair.

- If any part of the experimental design might cause significant **inaccuracies** in the results, the experiment will not be valid.

- Ideally, experiments should provide **repeatable** and **reproducible** results. If they do not, it does not mean that the experiment is invalid, unless the variations are very large. It does mean that it is difficult to make a confident conclusion, however.

Fair testing

- In an experiment one variable (the independent variable) should be changed by the experimenter.

- All other variables (apart from the dependent variable, which is being measured) should be controlled.

- Sometimes a variable cannot be controlled. In such cases, the effect of it will need to be taken into account when analysing the results.

Mathematical skills   Revised ☐

Percentages

Percent means parts per hundred. It is calculated as follows:

$$\text{percent (\%)} = \frac{\text{number in the category}}{\text{total number}} \times \frac{100}{1}$$

For example, if 5 seeds survive and grow out of 1125 produced by a plant,

$$\text{percentage survival} = \frac{5}{1125} \times \frac{100}{1} = 0.44\%$$

Means

To calculate a mean, add up all the values and divide by the number of values.

For example, if you have results of 5, 4, 4, 6, 4, 3, the total of the 6 values is 26.

The mean is $\frac{26}{6} = 4.3$

> **Examiner tip**
>
> With mathematical questions, you often get a mark for showing your working. If you get the right answer but do not show your working, you may lose a mark.

Calculating rates

From a graph, a rate of change can be calculated by measuring the slope of the graph.

The rate here is A ÷ B. The units would be units of A per unit of B. For example, if A was volume in mm³ and B was time in seconds, the units would be mm³/s.

Equations

Equations often have to be manipulated, particularly in physics. For instance, in the equation speed $= \dfrac{\text{distance}}{\text{time}}$, you may be asked to calculate the speed, the distance or the time. The way this is done is shown below.

$$\text{speed} = \frac{\text{distance}}{\text{time}}$$

To find the distance, multiply both sides by time:

$$\textbf{speed} \quad \textbf{x} \quad \textbf{time} \quad = \quad \frac{\textbf{distance}}{\text{time}}$$

SO ... speed x time = distance

OR ... **distance = speed x time**

To find the time, first multiply both sides by time:

$$\textbf{speed} \quad \textbf{x} \quad \textbf{time} \quad = \quad \frac{\textbf{distance}}{\text{time}}$$

Then divide both sides by speed:

$$\text{speed} \quad \textbf{x} \quad \textbf{time} \quad = \quad \frac{\textbf{distance}}{\textbf{speed}}$$

SO ... **time** $= \dfrac{\textbf{distance}}{\textbf{speed}}$

Check your understanding

Tested

You will find other questions testing these skills throughout this revision guide.

1   Scientists were testing 5 samples of water, A–E, for hardness. 1 cm³ of soap solution was shaken for 10 seconds with 10 cm³ of water sample **A**. The height of the froth was measured.

The experiment was then repeated with water samples **B, C, D** and **E**. State **two** ways that the scientists made sure that the investigation was a fair test.   *(2 marks)*

2   Use the equation **voltage = current × resistance** to calculate the resistance (in Ω) of a lamp when the voltage is 4 V and the current is 1.6 A. Show your working.   *(2 marks)*

3   A scientist carried out an experiment. Using a thermometer, she recorded the temperature of living seeds in a flask for 9 days.

   a) Why was it important that she used a vacuum (Thermos) flask?   *(1 mark)*

   b) Why was cotton wool used instead of a rubber stopper?   *(2 marks)*

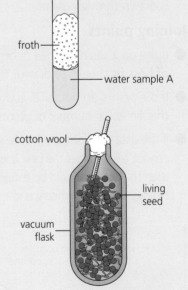

Go online for answers   Online

Drawing and using graphs

Exam questions involving graphs may ask you to:

● Draw a graph.

● Add points or sets of data to an existing graph.

● Read information from a graph.

● Describe the data and identify trends.

● Explain how the trends come about, using scientific knowledge.

Drawing graphs
Revised

Axes

● If you have to draw the axes, remember that the **independent variable** (the thing you change) goes on the horizontal (X) axis, and the **dependent variable** (the thing you measure) goes on the vertical (Y) axis.

● Axes must have **labels** which include **units**.

● The range of values on each axis must be **linear**. That is, one square on the graph paper must represent the same quantity, all the way along the axis.

● You should use as much of the graph paper as possible, as long as it does not make the scale on your axis difficult to use.

Plotting points

● The points on the graph must be plotted correctly. They should be no more than half of a small square out.

● Mark the points with a cross, so that the points are visible when a line is drawn through them.

Joining points

● If the data clearly follows either a straight line or a smooth curve, **a line of best fit** should be drawn. The term 'line of best fit' includes curves.

● If the points do not fall exactly on a line, the line should be drawn so that an equal number of points fall on either side.

● If the data does not seem to lie along a straight line or a curve (or if you cannot tell whether the best line of best fit would be a line or a curve) then the points should be connected with a ruler. This is more common in biology than in chemistry, and quite rare in physics.

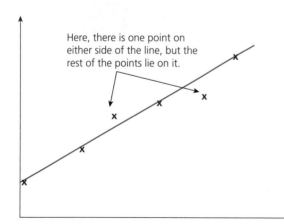

Here, there is one point on either side of the line, but the rest of the points lie on it.

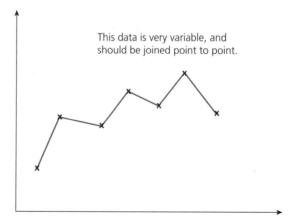

This data is very variable, and should be joined point to point.

Describing the data means that you should say what has happened, whereas explaining the data means that you must say what has caused it to happen.

Describing

When describing, you should describe the shape of the graph in terms of the variables, for example:

'As the (insert independent variable here) increases, the (insert dependent variable here) increases/decreases/stays the same.'

If the trend changes you must describe the change and indicate the point at which it occurred. For example:

'As the concentration increased, the rate of reaction increased, up to 2 M, and then it levelled off.'

> **Examiner tip**
>
> Whenever you are talking about graphs, use **actual** values from the axes to describe the part of the graph you are talking about.

Explaining

Explaining means that you must use scientific knowledge to say why the results show the pattern that they do, for example:

'After a meal, the blood glucose level goes up because there will be carbohydrates in the food. Later, the level goes down again because the body is using the glucose for respiration.'

Check your understanding — Tested

You will find other questions involving the interpretation of graphs throughout this revision guide.

4 A hydroelectric power station can be used to supply extra electricity when the rest of the power stations cannot supply enough. The demand for electricity changes throughout the day in the way shown below.

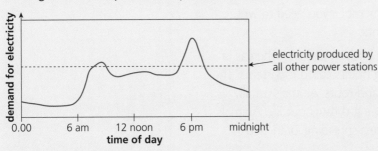

a) The demand for electricity is greatest around 6 pm. At what other time is demand greater than the supply from all other power stations? *(1 mark)*

b) Give **one** reason why the demand for electricity is highest at these times. *(1 mark)*

5 The graph shows the effect of temperature on the digestion of starch by amylase enzyme.

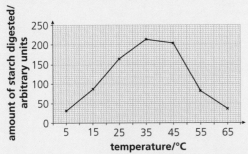

a) Describe the effect of temperature on the action of this enzyme. *(2 marks)*

b) Explain the results obtained between 35 and 65 °C. *(2 marks)*

Go online for answers — Online

'Quality of Written Communication' questions

Every exam paper will have at least one 'Quality of Written Communication' question (Higher-tier papers have two). They are always worth **6 marks**, and the marks are given for **how well you explain yourself** and for correct **spelling**, **grammar** and **punctuation**. In this book, these questions always have 'QWC' next to the number of marks.

The mark scheme for each of these questions is basically the same, although obviously the science will vary. The appropriate science is called **indicative content** in the mark scheme. The indicative content is given in the mark scheme in bullet points, but you should **always** write your answers in extended prose.

Here is an example of a QWC question, a student's answer and how it would be marked.

Question

Plants have a different pattern of growth and development to animals. Describe how plant growth differs from animal growth, and the advantages to plants of this form of growth. **(6 marks QWC)**

Mark scheme ——————————————————————————— Revised ☐

Indicative content

This is the science that might be used in the answer to the question above, but not *all* of this has to be used. Remember, you need to write your answer in full sentences, **not** bullet points.

Reference to the growth of all regions of the body in animals, whereas in plants growth is restricted to special growing points called meristems. The main meristems are at the tips of the stems and roots. Animals usually grow to a finite size but plants continue growing throughout life. Animals have a compact growth form but plants have a spreading, branched growth form.

Advantages to plants include:

● Plants cannot move and so are likely to be eaten – continual growth allows replacement of damaged parts.

● Branching growth form provides a large surface area for gas exchange and light absorption.

● Meristems direct growth mostly upwards (towards light) and downwards (towards water).

Level criteria

5–6 marks	The candidate constructs an articulate, integrated account correctly linking relevant points, such as those in the indicative content, which shows sequential reasoning. The answer fully addresses the question with no irrelevant inclusions or significant omissions. The candidate uses appropriate scientific terminology and accurate spelling, punctuation and grammar.
3–4 marks	The candidate constructs an account correctly linking some relevant points, such as those in the indicative content, showing some reasoning. The answer addresses the question with some omissions. The candidate uses mainly appropriate scientific terminology and some accurate spelling, punctuation and grammar.
1–2 marks	The candidate makes some relevant points, such as those in the indicative content, showing limited reasoning. The answer addresses the question with significant omissions. The candidate uses limited scientific terminology and inaccuracies in spelling, punctuation and grammar.
0 marks	The candidate does not make any attempt or give a relevant answer worthy of credit.

Sample answer

Revised ☐

Plants grow only at the top and bottom but animals grow all over. Plants are branched but animals are not. Its a good thing that plants grow the way they do because they need to absorb light for photosythysis and when animals eat their leaves they can grow new ones to replace them. Plants grow in length because they don't really need to grow outwards.

Examiner's comment and marks

The pupil's answer is **scientifically correct**, but not very clearly explained (e.g. 'plants grow the way they do' does not describe what features of growth the candidate is referring to; why don't they need to grow 'outwards'?). Some things have been left out (e.g. plants continue growing whereas animals grow to a certain size then stop; branched growth provides a larger surface area for absorption of light and gas exchange). There are **no irrelevant comments**, but the points are not clearly linked together in a **logical sequence**. There is little use of **scientific terminology** ('meristems' and 'compact growth form' could have been used). There is a **punctuation error** (its instead of it's) and a **spelling error** – photosythysis.

The answer seems to fit best with the 1–2 mark band and would be awarded 2 marks because there are relatively few spelling, punctuation and grammar errors and some linking of points. It is therefore worth a mark at the top end of this band.

> **Examiner tip**
>
> With these questions, remember:
> - Be careful with spelling, grammar and punctuation.
> - Try to put your ideas in a logical sequence, so that each idea follows on from the last one.
> - Use scientific terminology wherever you can
> - Explain your ideas carefully, so that they are easily understood.
> - Write in full sentences and paragraphs; do not use bullet points.

The **Check your understanding** sections throughout this book give a lot of examples of the types of QWC questions that might be asked in an exam. Use them as practice and, if possible, get someone else to tell you if you've explained the ideas clearly (because it's difficult to judge your own writing).

Equations and units for Foundation-tier papers

Physics 1

energy transfer = power × time	$E = Pt$
units used (kWh) = power (kW) × time (h)	
cost = units used × cost per unit	
% efficiency = $\dfrac{\text{useful energy (or power) transfer}}{\text{total energy (or power) input}} \times 100$	
density = $\dfrac{\text{mass}}{\text{volume}}$	$\rho = \dfrac{m}{V}$
wave speed = wavelength × frequency	$v = \lambda f$
speed = $\dfrac{\text{distance}}{\text{time}}$	

Physics 2

power = voltage × current	$P = VI$
current = $\dfrac{\text{voltage}}{\text{resistance}}$	$I = \dfrac{V}{R}$
acceleration (or deceleration) = $\dfrac{\text{change in velocity}}{\text{time}}$	$a = \dfrac{\Delta v}{t}$
acceleration = gradient of a velocity-time graph	
momentum = mass × velocity	$p = mv$
resultant force = mass × acceleration	$F = ma$
force = $\dfrac{\text{change in momentum}}{\text{time}}$	$F = \dfrac{\Delta p}{t}$
work = force × distance	$W = Fd$

Physics 3

pressure = $\dfrac{\text{force}}{\text{area}}$	$p = \dfrac{F}{A}$
$v = u + at$ $x = \dfrac{1}{2}(u + v)t$	where: u = initial velocity t = time v = final velocity x = displacement a = acceleration

Units

1 kWh = 3.6 MJ

T (in k) = θ (in °C) + 273

SI multipliers

Prefix	Multiplier		Prefix	Multiplier
p	10^{-12}		k	10^{3}
n	10^{-9}		M	10^{6}
μ	10^{-6}		G	10^{9}
m	10^{-3}		T	10^{12}

Equations and units for Higher-tier papers

Physics 1

power = voltage × current	$P = VI$
energy transfer = power × time	$E = Pt$
units used (kWh) = power (kW) × time (h)	
cost = units used × cost per unit	
% efficiency = $\dfrac{\text{useful energy (or power) transfer}}{\text{total energy (or power) input}} \times 100$	
density = $\dfrac{\text{mass}}{\text{volume}}$	$\rho = \dfrac{m}{V}$
wave speed = wavelength × frequency	$v = \lambda f$
speed = $\dfrac{\text{distance}}{\text{time}}$	

Physics 2

current = $\dfrac{\text{voltage}}{\text{resistance}}$	$I = \dfrac{V}{R}$
power = current^2 × resistance	$P = I^2R$
acceleration (or deceleration) = $\dfrac{\text{change in velocity}}{\text{time}}$	$a = \dfrac{\Delta v}{t}$
acceleration = gradient of a velocity-time graph	
distance travelled = area of a velocity-time graph	
momentum = mass × velocity	$p = mv$
resultant force = mass × acceleration	$F = ma$
force = $\dfrac{\text{change in momentum}}{\text{time}}$	$F = \dfrac{\Delta p}{t}$
work = force × distance	$W = Fd$
kinetic energy = $\dfrac{\text{mass} \times \text{speed}^2}{2}$	$KE = \frac{1}{2} mv^2$
change in potential energy = mass × gravitational field strength × height	$PE = mgh$

Physics 3

$\dfrac{\text{primary coil voltage}}{\text{secondary coil voltage}} = \dfrac{\text{primary coil turns}}{\text{secondary coil turns}}$	$\dfrac{V_1}{V_2} = \dfrac{N_1}{N_2}$
$v = u + at$	where:
$x = \frac{1}{2}(u + v)t$	u = initial velocity
$v^2 = u^2 + 2ax$	v = final velocity a = acceleration
$x = ut + \frac{1}{2}at^2$	t = time x = displacement
pressure = $\dfrac{\text{force}}{\text{area}}$	$p = \dfrac{F}{A}$
$\dfrac{pV}{T}$ = constant	where : p = pressure V = volume T = kelvin temperature
$E = mc^2$	

Index